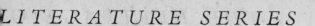

LITERATURE SERIES

ESSAYS AND BELLES LETTRES

Lighter Essays
Still Lighter Essays
Essays and Sketches
English Essayists
New and Old Essays, 1820–1935
More Modern Essays
Essays by Modern Writers
Modern Prose

The Art of the Essayist

POETRY

The Poet's Way *(Double Volume)*
The Poets' Company *(Double Volume)*
The Poets' Way Stage I
The Poets' Way Stage II
The Poet's Path
Narrative Poems
Modern Poetry
The Poets' Company
An Anthology of Longer Poems
to the 19th Century
The Poets' Harvest
Ballads and Narrative Poems

The Ambleside Book of Verse *(Double Volume)*

Contemporary Verse

MYTHS AND LEGENDS

Legends and Myths of Greece and Rome
A Heritage of Wonder Stories
Tales of the Greek Heroes

F

Tell Me Another *b*
Thrilling Tales of A
Afke's Ten *by Hicht*

George Turner.
10 c2

IF LOST Return

To Home Room 21 2 or

Office.

*The Heritage of
Literature Series*

SECTION A NO. 45

THE AMBLESIDE
BOOK OF VERSE

George Turner

1953.

ANTHOLOGIES OF POETRY
SELECTED BY E. W. PARKER, M.C.

THE POETS' PATH
THE POETS' WAY. Stage 1
THE POETS' WAY. Stage 2
THE POETS' WAY. Complete
THE POETS' HARVEST
THE POETS' COMPANY (to 19th century)
MODERN POETRY
THE POETS' COMPANY. Complete
A PAGEANT OF ENGLISH VERSE
A PAGEANT OF MODERN VERSE
NARRATIVE POEMS

THE AMBLESIDE
BOOK OF VERSE

Chosen and Edited
by
E. W. PARKER, M.C.

LONGMANS, GREEN AND CO
LONDON · NEW YORK · TORONTO

LONGMANS, GREEN AND CO LTD
6 & 7 CLIFFORD STREET LONDON W I

ALSO AT MELBOURNE AND CAPE TOWN

LONGMANS, GREEN AND CO INC
55 FIFTH AVENUE NEW YORK 3

LONGMANS, GREEN AND CO
215 VICTORIA STREET TORONTO I

ORIENT LONGMANS LTD
BOMBAY CALCUTTA MADRAS

First published 1949
New Impression 1949
New Impression 1951

PRINTED IN GREAT BRITAIN BY
NORTHUMBERLAND PRESS LIMITED
GATESHEAD ON TYNE

FOREWORD

WHAT are the eternal objects of poetry? Matthew Arnold answered the question by declaring that they are "actions; human actions; possessing an inherent merit in themselves, and which are communicated in an interesting manner by the art of the poet."

That there is truth in this is shown by the fact that most of the poetry which has come down to us from the earliest times is in the form of a narrative of action, and these epics, narrative poems and ballads never stale, but bring to each succeeding generation of readers the same joy in their fresh vigour and their stark passionate beauty.

Although it is convenient to distinguish between one kind of poetry and another, the essential poetry remains the same, whatever the form, as can be seen readily enough by comparing the poems included in the different groups in this volume. In making such comparisons one cannot fail to notice how frequently the deliberate literary artist has been influenced by the unknown singer of ballads who depended on his skill in the art of entertainment for his daily bread.

With the advent of the novelist most stories have been written, not in verse, but in prose, and the exceptions have had to compete with an ever-increasing flow of prose fiction. It is therefore not surprising that the narrative poems which have survived are often of outstanding beauty and compelling interest.

Ever since the amazing burst of song in the age of Elizabeth, the poet has become more conscious of himself as a literary artist and has pondered over his experiences, waiting for the inspiration that will create the perfect lyric. Just how such flashes of intuition come to the poet is a mystery, and when he occasionally lifts the curtain and allows us to catch a glimpse of him at work, it is fascinating to observe his methods, as for example when Wordsworth explains how he noticed:

> *A host of golden daffodils;*
> *Beside the lake, beneath the trees,*
> *Fluttering and dancing in the breeze.*

At first he saw them as we might have done:

> *I gazed—and gazed—but little thought*
> *What wealth the show to me had brought.*

Then in the lines that follow he gives us a picture of the literary craftsman at work:

> *For oft when on my couch I lie*
> *In vacant or in pensive mood,*
> *They flash upon that inward eye*
> *Which is the bliss of solitude;*
> *And then my heart with pleasure fills,*
> *And dances with the daffodils.*

To Wordsworth poetry was "emotion recollected in tranquillity," and in this volume there are examples from the work of other poets whose methods are similar. Yet for all his cunning craftsmanship the poet must wait for a flash of genius before the perfect lyric can emerge from his mind and take shape in "the best words in the best order."

ACKNOWLEDGEMENTS

Acknowledgement is due to the following for permission to reproduce copyright material:

Messrs. Gerald Duckworth & Co. Ltd. and Mr. Hilaire Belloc for " Tarantella " from *Sonnets and Verse;* Mr. Edmund Blunden for " The Midnight Skaters " from *Poems* and for " Spring is Coming " from *Poems of John Clare,* both originally published by Cobden Sanderson Ltd.; Messrs. Chatto & Windus for " Anthem for Doomed Youth " from *Poems of Wilfred Owen;* Messrs. J. M. Dent & Sons Ltd. for " The Donkey " from *Collected Poems of G. K. Chesterton,* and the executrix of the late G. K. Chesterton for " Lepanto " from *Collected Poems* published by Hollis & Carter Ltd.; The Clarendon Press, Oxford, for versions of " The Gay Goshawk," " Lord Randal " and " Sir Patrick Spens " from *The Oxford Book of Ballads;* Mr. Padraic Colum, Messrs. Macmillan & Co. and the Macmillan Company of New York for " The Old Woman of the Roads " from *Poems;* The Richards Press and the author's executors for " A Runnable Stag " from *Holiday and Other Poems* by John Davidson; Mrs. W. H. Davies and Messrs. Jonathan Cape Ltd. for " The Kingfisher " and " Rich Days " from *Collected Poems of W. H. Davies;* Mr. Walter de la Mare and Messrs. Faber & Faber Ltd. for " The Three Beggars," " The Silver Penny " and " Silver " from *Collected Rhymes;* Messrs. Secker & Warburg Ltd. and the author's executors for " The Parrot " and " The Dying Patriot " from *Collected Poems of James Elroy Flecker;* Mr. W. W. Gibson and Messrs. Macmillan & Co. Ltd. for " The Lighthouse " from *Collected Poems 1905-1925;* The Trustees of the Hardy Estate and Messrs. Macmillan & Co. Ltd. for " The Oxen " and " Weathers " from *Collected Poems of Thomas Hardy;* Mr. Ralph Hodgson and Messrs. Macmillan & Co. Ltd. for " Time, You Old Gipsy Man " from *Poems;* Sir Shane Leslie for " Fleet Street "; The Society of Authors, Dr. John Masefield, O.M., and The Macmillan Company of New York for " The Rider at the Gate," " Sea Fever " and " Wild Duck " from *Collected Poems* (copyright 1935 by John Masefield); Messrs. McClelland and Stewart Ltd.

ACKNOWLEDGEMENTS

for "The Joys of the Road" from *Poems by W. Bliss Carman*; Messrs. Methuen & Co. Ltd. for "Smells" from *Chimney Smoke* by Christopher Morley; Mrs. Monro for "Milk for the Cat" by Harold Monro; Mr. Alfred Noyes and Messrs. Wm. Blackwood & Sons Ltd. for "The Ballad of Dick Turpin" from *Collective Poems*; Mrs. Skrine and Messrs. Wm. Blackwood & Sons Ltd. for "Corrymeela" from *Songs of the Glens of Antrim* by Moira O'Neill; Mr. Seumas O'Sullivan for "In Mercer Street" from *Collected Poems* published by the Orwell Press 1940; The Oxford University Press for "The Stream's Song" from *Poems of Lascelles Abercrombie*; Lady Quiller-Couch for "Sage Counsel" by Sir Arthur Quiller-Couch; Mr. Diarmuid Russell and Messrs. Macmillan & Co. Ltd. for "Frolic" from *Collected Poems of A.E.*; Messrs. Sidgwick & Jackson Ltd. for "The Hill" from *Collected Poems of Rupert Brooke*, and "The Blackbird" and "The Vagabond" from *Collected Poems of John Drinkwater*; Mr. Stephen Spender and Messrs. Faber & Faber Ltd. for "The Landscape near an Aerodrome" from *Poems*; Mr. James Stephens and Messrs. Macmillan & Co. Ltd. for "The Snare" from *Collected Poems*; Mrs. H. Thomas and Messrs. Faber & Faber Ltd. for "Words" from *Collected Poems of Edward Thomas*; Mrs. W. B. Yeats and Messrs. Macmillan & Co. Ltd. for "The Lake Isle of Innisfree," "The Fiddler of Dooney" and "The Ballad of Father Gilligan" from *Collected Poems of W. B. Yeats*; Mr. Andrew Young and Messrs. Jonathan Cape Ltd. for "A Windy Day" from *Collected Poems of Andrew Young*.

CONTENTS

BALLADS

BALLADS AND SONGS OF JACOBITE TIMES

HUMOUR

CONTENTS

NARRATIVE POEMS

CONTENTS

PICTURES FROM LONGER POEMS

xiii

CONTENTS

xiv

CONTENTS

xv

CONTENTS

xvi

BALLADS

THE BONNY EARL OF MORAY

Ye Highlands and ye Lawlands,
  O where hae ye been?
They hae slain the Earl of Moray,
  And hae laid him on the green.

Now wae be to thee, Huntley!
  And whairfore did ye sae!
I bade you bring him wi' you,
  But forbade you him to slay.

He was a braw gallant,
  And he rid at the ring;
And the bonny Earl of Moray,
  O he might hae been a king!

He was a braw gallant,
  And he play'd at the ba';
And the bonny Earl of Moray
  Was the flower amang them a'!

He was a braw gallant,
  And he play'd at the gluve;
And the bonny Earl of Moray,
  O he was the Queen's luve!

O lang will his Lady
    Look owre the Castle Downe,
Ere she see the Earl of Moray
    Come sounding through the town!

ANONYMOUS

BONNIE GEORGE CAMPBELL

Hie upon Hielands,
    And laigh upon Tay,
Bonnie George Campbell
    Rode out on a day.

He saddled, he bridled,
    And gallant rode he,
And hame cam his guid horse,
    But never cam he.

Out cam his mother dear,
    Greetin' fu sair,
And out cam his bonnie bryde,
    Rivin' her hair.

" The meadow lies green,
    The corn is unshorn,
But bonnie George Campbell
    Will never return."

Saddled and bridled
    And booted rode he,
A plume in his helmet,
    A sword at his knee.

> But toom cam his saddle,
>   All bloody to see,
> Oh, hame cam his guid horse,
>   But never cam he!

ıaigh] low.   greetin'] lamenting.   rivin'] tearing.   toom] empty.

ROBIN HOOD AND ALAN A DALE

Come listen to me, you gallants so free,
  All you that love mirth for to hear,
And I will you tell of a bold outláw,
  That lived in Nottinghamshire.

As Robin Hood in the forest stood,
  All under the green-wood tree,
There was he ware of a brave young man,
  As fine as fine might be.

The youngster was clothed in scarlet red,
  In scarlet fine and gay,
And he did frisk it over the plain,
  And chanted a roundelay.

As Robin Hood next morning stood,
  Amongst the leaves so gay,
There did he espy the same young man
  Come drooping along the way.

The scarlet he wore the day before,
  It was clean cast away;
And every step he fetched a sigh,
  " Alack and a well a day! "

3

Then steppèd forth brave Little John,
  And Much the miller's son,
Which made the young man bend his bow,
  When as he saw them come.

"Stand off, stand off!" the young man said,
  "What is your will with me?"—
"You must come before our master straight,
  Under yon green-wood tree."

And when he came bold Robin before,
  Robin asked him courteously,
"O hast thou any money to spare,
  For my merry men and me?"

"I have no money," the young man said,
  "But five shillings and a ring;
And that I have kept this seven long years,
  To have it at my wedding.

"Yesterday I should have married a maid,
  But she is now from me ta'en,
And chosen to be an old knight's delight,
  Whereby my poor heart is slain."

"What is thy name?" then said Robin Hood,
  "Come tell me, without any fail."—
"By the faith of my body," then said the
    young man,
  "My name it is Alan a Dale."

"What wilt thou give me," said Robin Hood,
  "In ready gold or fee,

To help thee to thy true-love again,
  And deliver her unto thee? "

" I have no money," then quoth the young man,
  " No ready gold nor fee,
But I will swear upon a book
  Thy true servant for to be."—

" But how many miles to thy true-love?
  Come tell me without any guile."—
" By the faith of my body," then said the
    young man,
  " It is but five little mile."

Then Robin he hasted over the plain,
  He did neither stint nor lin,
Until he came unto the church
  Where Alan should keep his wedding.

" What dost thou do here? " the Bishop he
    said,
  " I prithee now tell to me."
" I am a bold harper," quoth Robin Hood,
  " And the best in the north country."

" O welcome, O welcome! " the Bishop he said,
  " That music best pleaseth me."—
" You shall have no music," quoth Robin Hood,
  " Till the bride and the bridegroom I see."

stint nor lin] tarry, delay.

5

With that came in a wealthy knight,
  Which was both grave and old,
And after him a finikin lass,
  Did shine like glistering gold.

"This is no fit match," quoth bold Robin
    Hood,
  "That you do seem to make here;
For since we are come unto the church,
  The bride she shall choose her own dear."

Then Robin Hood put his horn to his mouth,
  And blew blasts two or three;
When four and twenty bowmen bold
  Come leaping over the lee.

And when they came into the churchyard,
  Marching all on a row,
The first man was Alan a Dale,
  To give bold Robin his bow.

"This is thy true-love," Robin he said,
  "Young Alan, as I hear say;
And you shall be married at this same time,
  Before we depart away."

"That shall not be," the Bishop he said,
  "For thy word it shall not stand;
They shall be three times asked in the church,
  As the law is of our land."

finikin] dainty.

Robin Hood pull'd off the Bishop's coat,
   And put it upon Little John;
"By the faith of my body," then Robin said,
   "The cloth doth make thee a man."

When Little John went into the choir,
   The people began for to laugh;
He asked them seven times in the church,
   Lest three should not be enough.

"Who gives me this maid?" then said Little
     John.
   Quoth Robin, "That do I!
And he that doth take her from Alan a Dale
   Full dearly he shall her buy."

And thus having ended this merry wedding,
   The bride looked as fresh as a queen,
And so they returned to the merry green-wood,
   Amongst the leaves so green.

ANONYMOUS

SIR PATRICK SPENS

I. *The Sailing*

The king sits in Dunfermline town
   Drinking the blude-red wine;
"O whare will I get a skeely skipper
   To sail this new ship o' mine?"

O up and spak an eldern knight,
  Sat at the king's right knee;
" Sir Patrick Spens is the best sailor
  That ever sail'd the sea."

Our king has written a braid letter,
  And seal'd it with his hand,
And sent it to Sir Patrick Spens,
  Was walking on the strand.

" To Noroway, to Noroway,
  To Noroway o'er the faem;
The king's daughter o' Noroway,
  'Tis thou must bring her hame."

The first word that Sir Patrick read
  So loud, loud laugh'd he;
The neist word that Sir Patrick read
  The tear blinded his e'e.

" O wha is this has done this deed
  And tauld the king o' me,
To send us out, at this time o' year,
  To sail upon the sea?

" Be it wind, be it weet, be it hail, be it sleet,
  Our ship must sail the faem;
The king's daughter o' Noroway,
  'Tis we must fetch her hame."

They hoysed their sails on Monenday morn
  Wi' a' the speed they may;
They hae landed in Noroway
  Upon a Wodensday.

II. *The Return*

"Mak ready, mak ready, my merry men a'!
   Our gude ship sails the morn."
"Now ever alack, my master dear,
   I fear a deadly storm.

"I saw the new moon late yestreen
   Wi' the auld moon in her arm;
And if we gang to sea, master,
   I fear we'll come to harm."

They hadna sail'd a league, a league,
   A league, but barely three,
When the lift grew dark, and the wind blew loud
   And gurly grew the sea.

The ankers brak, and the topmast lap,
   It was sic a deadly storm:
And the waves cam owre the broken ship
   Till a' her sides were torn.

"O where will I get a gude sailor
   To tak' my helm in hand,
Till I get up to the tall topmast
   To see if I can spy land?"

"O here am I, a sailor gude,
   To tak' the helm in hand,
Till you go up to the tall topmast,
   But I fear you'll ne'er spy land."

lift] the sky.

He hadna gane a step, a step,
  A step but barely ane,
When a bolt flew out of our goodly ship,
  And the saut sea it came in.

" Go fetch a web o' the silken claith,
  Another o' the twine,
And wap them into our ship's side,
  And let nae the sea come in."

They fetch'd a web o' the silken claith,
  Another o' the twine,
And they wapp'd them round that gude ship's
    side,
  But still the sea came in.

O laith, laith were our gude Scots lords
  To wet their cork-heel'd shoon;
But lang or a' the play was play'd
  They wat their hats aboon.

And mony was the feather bed
  That flatter'd on the faem;
And mony was the gude lord's son
  That never mair cam hame.

O lang, lang may the ladies sit,
  Wi' their fans into their hand,
Before they see Sir Patrick Spens
  Come sailing to the strand!

And lang, lang may the maidens sit
  Wi' their gowd kames in their hair

A-waiting for their ain dear loves!
　For them they'll see nae mair.

Half owre, half owre to Aberdour
　'Tis fifty fathoms deep;
And there lies gude Sir Patrick Spens
　Wi' the Scots lords at his feet!

ANONYMOUS

THE DAEMON LOVER

" O where have you been, my long, long love,
　This long seven years and more? "—
" O I'm come to seek my former vows
　Ye granted me before."—

" O hold your tongue of your former vows,
　For they will breed sad strife;
O hold your tongue of your former vows,
　For I am become a wife."

He turned him right and round about,
　And the tear blinded his ee;
" I wad never hae trodden on Irish ground
　If it had not been for thee.

I might hae had a king's daughter,
　Far, far beyond the sea;
I might have had a king's daughter,
　Had it not been for love o' thee."

" If ye might have had a king's daughter,
    Yer sell ye had to blame;
Ye might have taken the king's daughter,
    For ye kend that I was nane!

If I was to leave my husband dear,
    And my two babes also,
O what have you to take me to,
    If with you I should go? "

" I hae seven ships upon the sea;
    The eighth brought me to land,
With four and twenty bold mariners,
    And music on every hand."

She has taken up her two little babes,
    Kissed them both cheek and chin;
" O fare ye well, my own two babes,
    For I'll never see you again."

She set her foot upon the ship;
    No mariners could she behold,
But the sails were o' the taffetie,
    And the masts o' the beaten gold.

She had not sailed a league, a league,
    A league but barely three,
When dismal grew his countenance,
    And drumlie grew his ee.

They had not sailed a league, a league,
    A league but barely three,
Until she espied his cloven foot,
    And she wept right bitterly.

drumlie] gloomy.

12

" O hold your tongue of your weeping," says he,
  " Of your weeping now let me be;
I will show you how the lilies grow
  On the banks of Italy! "—

" O what hills are yon, yon pleasant hills,
  That the sun shines sweetly on? "
" O yon are the hills of heaven," he said,
  " Where you will never win."—

" O whaten a mountain is yon," she said,
  " All so dreary wi' frost and snow? "
" O yon is the mountain of hell," he cried,
  " Where you and I will go."

He strack the tap-mast wi' his hand,
  The fore-mast wi' his knee;
And he brake that gallant ship in twain,
  And sank her in the sea.

ANONYMOUS

LORD RANDAL

" O, where hae ye been, Lord Randal, my son?
O, where hae ye been, my handsome young man? "—
" I have been to the wild wood; mother, make my bed
    soon,
For I'm weary wi' hunting, and fain wald lie down."

" Where gat ye your dinner, Lord Randal, my son?
Where gat ye your dinner, my handsome young man? "—
" I dined wi' my true-love; mother, make my bed soon,
For I'm weary wi' hunting, and fain wald lie down."

13

" What gat ye to your dinner, Lord Randal, my son?
What gat ye to your dinner, my handsome young
   man? "—
" I gat eels boiled in bro'; mother, make my bed soon,
For I'm weary wi' hunting, and fain wald lie down."

" What became of your bloodhounds, Lord Randal, my
   son?
" What became of your bloodhounds, my handsome
   young man? "—
" O, they swell'd and they died; mother, make my bed
   soon,
For I'm weary wi' hunting, and fain wald lie down."

" O, I fear ye are poison'd, Lord Randal, my son!
O, I fear ye are poison'd, my handsome young man! "—
" O, yes, I am poison'd; mother, make my bed soon,
For I'm sick at the heart, and I fain wald lie down."
ANONYMOUS

THE GAY GOSHAWK

I

" O well 's me o' my gay goss-hawk,
   That he can speak and flee!
He'll carry a letter to my love,
   Bring back another to me."—

II

" O how can I your true-love ken,
   Or how can I her know?

Whan frae her mouth I never heard couth,
  Nor wi' my eyes her saw."—

III

" O well sall ye my true-love ken,
  As soon as you her see;
For, of a' the flow'rs in fair England,
  The fairest flow'r is she.

IV

" At even at my love's bower-door
  There grows a bowing birk,
An' sit ye down and sing thereon,
  As she gangs to the kirk.

V

" An' four-and-twenty ladies fair
  Will wash and go to kirk,
But well sall ye my true-love ken,
  For she wears gowd on her skirt.

VI

" An four-and-twenty gay ladies
  Will to the mass repair,
But well sall ye my true-love ken,
  For she wears gowd on her hair."

VII

O even at that lady's bower-door
  There grows a bowing birk,
An' he set down and sang thereon,
  As she gaed to the kirk.

couth] word.

15

VIII

" O eet and drink, my marys a',
The wine flows you among,
Till I gang to my shot-window,
An' hear yon bonny bird's song.

IX

" Sing on, sing on, my bonny bird,
The song ye sang the streen,
For I ken by your sweet singin'
You're frae my true-love sen."

X

O first he sang a merry song,
An' then he sang a grave,
An' then he peck'd his feathers gray,
To her the letter gave.

XI

" Ha, there's a letter frae your love,
He says he sent you three;
He canna wait your luve langer,
But for your sake he'll dee.

XII

" He bids you write a letter to him;
He says he's sent you five;
He canna wait your luve langer,
Tho' you're the fairest alive."—

marys] maidens.   shot-window] bow-window.
                the streen] yestreen.

XIII

" Ye bid him bake his bridal-bread,
    And brew his bridal-ale,
An' I'll meet him in fair Scotland
    Lang, lang or it be stale."

XIV

She's doen her to her father dear
    Fa'n low down on her knee:
" A boon, a boon, my father dear
    I pray you, grant it me! "—

XV

" Ask on, ask on, my daughter,
    An' granted it sall be:
Except ae squire in fair Scotland,
    An' him you sall never see."—

XVI

" The only boon, my father dear,
    That I do crave of thee,
Is, gin I die in southin lands,
    In Scotland to bury me.

XVII

" An' the firstin kirk that ye come till,
    Ye gar the bells be rung,
An' the nextin kirk that ye come till,
    Ye gar the mass be sung.

XVIII

" An' the thirdin kirk that ye come till,
    You deal gold for my sake,

17

An' the fourthin kirk that ye come till,
    You tarry there till night."

XIX

She is doen her to her bigly bow'r,
    As fast as she could fare,
An' she has tane a sleepy draught,
    That she had mixt wi' care.

XX

She's laid her down upon her bed,
    An' soon she's fa'n asleep,
And soon o'er every tender limb
    Cauld death began to creep.

XXI

When night was flown, an' day was come,
    Nae ane that did her see
But thought she was as surely dead
    As ony lady cou'd be.

XXII

Her father an' her brothers dear
    Gar'd make to her a bier;
The tae half was o' guid red gold,
    The tither o' silver clear.

XXIII

Her mither an' her sisters fair
    Gar'd work for her a sark;
The tae half was o' cambrick fine,
    The tither o' needle wark.

bigly] large.

18

XXIV

The firstin kirk that they came till.
  They gar'd the bells be rung,
An' the nextin kirk that they came till,
  They gar'd the mass be sung.

XXV

The thirdin kirk that they came till,
  They dealt gold for her sake,
An' the fourthin kirk that they came till,
  Lo, there they met her make!

XXVI

"Lay down, lay down the bigly bier,
  Lat me the dead look on!"—
Wi' cherry cheeks and ruby lips
  She lay and smil'd on him.

XXVII

"O ae sheave o' your bread, true-love,
  An' ae glass o' your wine!
For I hae fasted for your sake
  These fully days is nine.

XXVIII

"Gang hame, gang hame, my seven bold
    brothers,
  Gang hame and sound your horn;
An' ye may boast in southin lands
  Your sister's play'd you scorn!"

ANONYMOUS

make] lover.   sheave] slice.

EARL MAR'S DAUGHTER

It was intill a pleasant time,
    Upon a summer's day,
The noble Earl Mar's daughter
    Went forth to sport and play.

And as she play'd and sported
    Below a green oak tree,
There she saw a sprightly doo
    Set on a branch sae hie.

" O Coo-my-doo, my Love so true,
    If ye'll come down to me,
Ye'll have a cage of good red gold
    Instead o' simple tree.

" I'll put gold hingers roun' your cage,
    And siller round your wa';
I'll gar ye shine as fair a bird
    As any o' them a'."

And she had not these words well spoke,
    Nor yet these words well said,
Till Coo-my-doo flew from the tower
    And lighted on her head.

Then she had brought this pretty bird
    Home to her bowers and ha',
And made him shine as fair a bird
    As any o' them a'.

doo] dove.   hingers] hangings.   gar] make.
20

When day was gone and night was come,
    About the evening-tide,
This lady spied a sprightly youth
    Stand straight up by her side.

" O who are ye, young man? " she said,
    " What country come ye frae? "—
" I flew across the sea," he said,
    " 'Twas but this very day.

" My mither is a queen," he says,
    " Likewise of magic skill;
'Twas she that turn'd me in a doo,
    To fly where'er I will.

" And it was but this very day
    That I came o'er the sea:
I loved you at a single look;
    With you I'll live and dee."—

" O Coo-my-doo, my Love so true,
    No more from me ye'll gae——"
" That's never my intent, my Love:
    As ye said, it shall be sae."

Thus he has stay'd in bower with her
    For twenty years and three;
Till there came a lord of high renown
    To court this fair ladye.

But still his proffer she refused,
    And all his presents too;
Says, " I'm content to live alone
    With my bird Coo-my-doo."

Her father sware a solemn oath,
   Among the nobles all,
" To-morrow, ere I eat or drink,
   That bird I'll surely kill."

The bird was sitting in his cage,
   And heard what he did say;
He jump'd upon the window-sill:
   " 'Tis time I was away."

Then Coo-my-doo took flight and flew
   Beyond the raging sea,
And lighted at his mither's castle,
   On a tower of gold sae hie.

The Queen his mither was walking out,
   To see what she could see,
And there she saw her darling son
   Set on the tower sae hie.

" Get dancers here to dance," she said,
   " And minstrels for to play;
For here's my dear son Florentine
   Come hame wi' me to stay."—

" Instead of dancers to dance, mither,
   Or minstrels for to play,
Turn four-and-twenty well-wight men
   Like storks, in feathers gray;

" My seven sons in seven swans,
   Above their heads to flee;

well-wight] powerful, stalwart.

22

And I myself a gay goshawk,
  A bird o' high degree."

This flock of birds took flight and flew
  Beyond the raging sea;
They landed near the Earl Mar's castle,
  Took shelter in every tree.

These birds flew up from bush and tree,
  And lighted on the ha';
And when the wedding-train came forth,
  Flew down among them a'.

The storks they seized the boldest men,
  That they could nor fight nor flee;
The swans they bound the bridegroom fast
  Unto a green oak tree.

They flew around the bride-maidens,
  Then on the bride's own head;
And with the twinkling of an eye,
  The bride and they were fled.

ANONYMOUS

THE BATTLE OF OTTERBURN

It fell about the Lammas tide
  When the muir-men win their hay,
The doughty earl of Douglas rode
  Into England, to catch a prey.

He chose the Gordons and the Græmes,
    With them the Lindesays, light and gay:
But the Jardines wald not with him ride,
    And they rue it to this day.

And he has burn'd the dales of Tyne,
    And part of Bambrough shire;
And three good towers on Roxburgh fells,
    He left them all on fire.

And he march'd up to Newcastle,
    And rode it round about;
" O wha's the lord of this castle,
    Or wha's the lady o't? "

But up spake proud Lord Percy, then,
    And O but he spake hie!
" I am the lord of this castle,
    My wife's the lady gay."

" If thou'rt the lord of this castle,
    Sae weel it pleases me!
For, ere I cross the border fells,
    The tane of us shall die."

He took a long spear in his hand,
    Shod with the metal free,
And for to meet the Douglas there
    He rode right furiouslie.

But O how pale his lady look'd
    Frae aff the castle wa',
When down before the Scottish spear,
    She saw proud Percy fa'.

"Had we twa been upon the green,
　And never an eye to see,
I wad hae had you, flesh and fell;
　But your sword sall gae wi' me.

"But gae ye up to Otterburn,
　And wait there dayis three;
And, if I come not ere three dayis end,
　A fause knight ca' ye me."

"The Otterburn's a bonnie burn;
　'Tis pleasant there to be;
But there is nought at Otterburn
　To feed my men and me.

"The deer rins wild on hill and dale,
　The birds fly wild from tree to tree;
But there is neither bread nor kale
　To fend my men and me.

"Yet I will stay at Otterburn,
　Where you shall welcome be;
And, if ye come not at three dayis end,
　A fause lord I'll ca' thee."

"Thither will I come," proud Percy said,
　"By the might of Our Ladye!"—
"There will I bide thee," said the Douglas,
　"My trowth I plight to thee."

They lighted high on Otterburn,
　Upon the bent sae brown;
They lighted high on Otterburn,
　And threw their pallions down.

pallions] pavilions, tents.

25

And he that had a bonnie boy,
    Sent out his horse to grass;
And he that had not a bonnie boy,
    His ain servant he was.

But up then spake a little page,
    Before the peep of dawn—
"O waken ye, waken ye, my good lord,
    For Percy's hard at hand."

"Ye lie, ye lie, ye liar loud!
    Sae loud I hear ye lie:
For Percy had not men yestreen,
    To dight my men and me.

"But I hae dream'd a dreary dream,
    Beyond the Isle of Skye;
I saw a dead man win a fight,
    And I think that man was I."

He belted on his good braid sword,
    And to the field he ran;
But he forgot the helmet good,
    That should have kept his brain.

When Percy wi' the Douglas met,
    I wat he was fu' fain!
They swakk'd their swords, till sair they swat,
    And the blood ran down like rain.

But Percy with his good braid sword,
    That could so sharply wound,
Has wounded Douglas on the brow,
    Till he fell to the ground.

    swakk'd] exchanged blows.

Then he call'd on his little foot-page,
  And said—"Run speedilie,
And fetch my ain dear sister's son,
  Sir Hugh Montgomery."

"My nephew good," the Douglas said,
  "What recks the death of ane!
Last night I dream'd a dreary dream,
  And I ken the day's thy ain.

"My wound is deep; I fain would sleep;
  Take thou the vanguard of the three,
And hide me by the braken bush,
  That grows on yonder lilye lee.

"O bury me by the braken bush,
  Beneath the blooming briar,
Let never living mortal ken
  That ere a kindly Scot lies here."

He lifted up that noble lord,
  Wi' the saut tear in his e'e;
He hid him in the braken bush,
  That his merrie men might not see.

The moon was clear, the day drew near,
  The spears in flinders flew,
But many a gallant Englishman
  Ere day the Scotsmen slew.

The Gordons good, in English blood
  They steep'd their hose and shoon;
The Lindesays flew like fire about,
  Till all the fray was done.

27

The Percy and Montgomery met,
   That either of other were fain;
They swakkéd swords, and they twa swat,
   And aye the blude ran down between.

" Yield thee, O yield thee, Percy! " he said,
   " Or else I vow I'll lay thee low! "
" Whom to shall I yield," said Earl Percy.
   " Now that I see it must be so? "

" Thou shalt not yield to lord nor loun,
   Nor yet shalt thou yield to me;
But yield thee to the braken bush,
   That grows upon yon lilye lee! "

" I will not yield to a braken bush,
   Nor yet will I yield to a briar;
But I would yield to Earl Douglas,
   Or Sir Hugh the Montgomery, if he were
      here."

As soon as he knew it was Montgomery,
   He stuck his sword's point in the gronde;
And the Montgomery was a courteous knight,
   And quickly took him by the honde.

This deed was done at Otterburn,
   About the breaking of the day;
Earl Douglas was buried at the braken bush,
   And the Percy led captive away.

                                    ANONYMOUS

28

BALLADS AND SONGS
OF JACOBITE TIMES

HAME, HAME, HAME

Hame, hame, hame, O hame fain wad I be—
O hame, hame, hame, to my ain countree!

When the flower is i' the bud and the leaf is on the tree,
The larks shall sing me hame in my ain countree;
Hame, hame, hame, O hame fain wad I be—
O hame, hame, hame, to my ain countree!

The green leaf o' loyaltie's beginning for to fa',
The bonnie White Rose it is withering an' a';
But I'll water 't wi' the blude of usurping tyrannie,
An' green it will graw in my ain countree.

O, there's nocht now frae ruin my country can save,
But the keys o' kind heaven, to open the grave;
That a' the noble martyrs wha died for loyaltie
May rise again an' fight for their ain countree.

The great now are gane, a' wha ventured to save,
The new grass is springing on the tap o' their grave;
But the sun through the mirk blinks blythe in my 'ee
"I'll shine on ye yet in your ain countree."

Hame, hame, hame, O hame fain wad I be—
O hame, hame, hame, to my ain countree!

ALAN CUNNINGHAM

THE FAREWELL

It was a' for our rightfu' King
    We left fair Scotland's strand;
It was a' for our rightfu' King
    We e'er saw Irish land,
        My dear—
    We e'er saw Irish land.

Now a' is done that men can do,
    And a' is done in vain;
My love and native land, farewell,
    For I maun cross the main,
        My dear—
    For I maun cross the main.

He turn'd him right and round about
    Upon the Irish shore;
And gae his bridle-reins a shake,
    With, Adieu for evermore,
        My dear—
    With, Adieu for evermore!

The sodger frae the wars returns,
    The sailor frae the main;
But I hae parted frae my love,
    Never to meet again,
        My dear—
    Never to meet again.

When day is gane, and night is come,
   And a' folk bound to sleep,
I think on him that's far awa',
   The lee-lang night, and weep,
      My dear—
   The lee-lang night, and weep.

ROBERT BURNS

BONNIE PRINCE CHARLIE

Cam' ye by Athol, lad wi' the philabeg,
   Down by the Tummel, or banks of the Gary?
Saw ye our lads, wi' their bonnets and white cockades,
   Leaving their mountains to follow Prince Charlie?
Follow thee, follow thee, wha wadna follow thee?
   Lang hast thou loved and trusted us fairly!
Charlie, Charlie, wha wadna follow thee?
   King of the Highland hearts, bonnie Prince Charlie.

I ha'e but ae son, my brave young Donald;
   But if I had ten they should follow Glengarry;
Health to M'Donald and gallant Clan-Ronald,
   For these are the men that will die for their Charlie.
Follow thee, follow thee, wha wadna follow thee?
   Lang hast thou loved and trusted us fairly!
Charlie, Charlie, wha wadna follow thee?
   King of the Highland hearts, bonnie Prince Charlie.

I'll to Lochiel and Appin, and kneel to them;
   Down by Lord Murray and Roy of Kildarlie;
Brave Mackintosh he shall fly to the field wi' them:
   They are the lads I can trust wi' my Charlie.

Follow thee, follow thee, wha wadna follow thee?
  Lang hast thou loved and trusted us fairly!
Charlie, Charlie, wha wadna follow thee?
  King of the Highland hearts, bonnie Prince Charlie.

Down through the Lowlands, down wi' the whigamore,
  Loyal true Highlanders, down with them rarely;
Ronald and Donald drive on wi' the braid claymore,
  Over the necks of the foes of Prince Charlie.
Follow thee, follow thee, wha wadna follow thee?
  Lang hast thou loved and trusted us fairly!
Charlie, Charlie, wha wadna follow thee?
  King of the Highland hearts, bonnie Prince Charlie.

JAMES HOGG

WAE'S ME FOR PRINCE CHARLIE

A wee bird cam' to our ha' door,
  He warbled sweet and clearly,
An' aye the o'ercome o' his sang
  Was " Wae's me for Prince Charlie! "
Oh! when I heard the bonnie soun'
  The tears cam' happin' rarely,
I took my bannet aff my head,
  For weel I lo'ed Prince Charlie.

Quoth I, " My bird, my bonnie, bonnie bird.
  Is that a sang ye borrow,
Are these some words ye've learnt by heart,
  Or a lilt o' dool an' sorrow? "

" Oh! no no no," the wee bird sang,
    " I've flown sin' mornin' early.
But sic a day o' wind and rain—
    Oh! wae's me for Prince Charlie!

" On hills that are, by right, his ain
    He roves a lanely stranger,
On every side he's press'd by want
    On every side is danger;
Yestreen I met him in a glen,
    My heart maist burstit fairly,
For sadly chang'd indeed was he—
    Oh! wae's me for Prince Charlie!

" Dark night cam' on, the tempest roar'd
    Loud o'er the hills and valleys,
An' whare was't that your Prince lay down
    Whase hame should been a palace?
He row'd him in a Highland plaid,
    Which cover'd him but sparely,
An' slept beneath a bush o' broom—
    Oh! wae's me for Prince Charlie! "

But now the bird saw some red coats,
    An' he sheuk his wings wi' anger,
" Oh! this is no a land for me,
    I'll tarry here nae langer."
He hover'd on the wing a while
    Ere he departed fairly,
But weel I mind the farewell strain
    Was " Wae's me for Prince Charlie! "

                                        WILLIAM GLEN

WILL YE NO COME BACK AGAIN?

Bonnie Charlie's now awa',
   Safely ower the friendly main;
Mony a heart will break in twa
   Should he ne'er come back again?

   Will ye no come back again?
   Will ye no come back again?
   Better lo'ed ye canna be—
   Will ye no come back again?

Ye trusted in your Hieland men,
   They trusted you, dear Charlie!
They kent your hiding in the glen,
   Death or exile braving.
      Will ye no, etc.

English bribes were a' in vain,
   Tho' puir, and puirer, we maun be;
Siller canna buy the heart
   That beats aye for thine and thee.
      Will ye no, etc.

We watch'd thee in the gloamin' hour,
   We watch'd thee in the mornin' grey;
Though thirty thousand pound they gi'e,
   Oh, there is none that wad betray!
      Will ye no, etc.

Sweet's the laverock's note, and lang,
   Lilting wildly up the glen;
But aye to me he sings ae sang,
   Will ye no come back again?
      Will ye no, etc.   LADY NAIRNE

HUMOUR

THE WEE COOPER O' FIFE

There was a wee cooper who lived in Fife,
  Nickity, nackity, noo, noo, noo.
And he has gotten a gentle wife.
  Hey Willie Wallacky, how John Dougall,
  Alane, quo' Rushety, roue, roue, roue.

She wadna bake, nor she wadna brew,
For the spoiling o' her comely hue.

She wadna card, nor she wadna spin,
For the shaming o' her gentle kin.

She wadna wash, nor she wadna wring,
For the spoiling o' her gouden ring.

The cooper's awa to his woo-pack,
And has laid a sheep-skin on his wife's back.

"It's I'll no' thrash ye, for your proud kin,
But I will thrash my ain sheep-skin."

"Oh, I will bake, and I will brew,
And never mair think on my comely hue.

"Oh, I will card, and I will spin,
And never think mair on my gentle kin.

"Oh, I will wash, and I will wring,
And never mair think on my gouden ring."

A' ye wha hae gotten a gentle wife
Send ye for the wee cooper o' Fife.

ANONYMOUS

SAGE COUNSEL

The lion is the beast to fight:
   He leaps along the plain,
And if you run with all your might,
   He runs with all his mane.
      I'm glad I'm not a Hottentot,
      But if I were, with outward cal-lum
      I'd either faint upon the spot
      Or hie me up a leafy pal-lum.

The chamois is the beast to hunt:
   He's fleeter than the wind,
And when the chamois is in front
   The hunter is behind.
      The Tyrolese make famous cheese
      And hunt the chamois o'er the chazzums·
      I'd choose the former, if you please,
      For precipices give me spazzums.

The polar bear will make a rug
  Almost as white as snow:
But if he gets you in his hug,
  He rarely lets you go.
    And Polar ice looks very nice,
    With all the colours of a prissum:
    But, if you'll follow my advice,
    Stay home and learn your catechissum.

SIR ARTHUR QUILLER-COUCH

THE LOBSTER QUADRILLE

" Will you walk a little faster? " said a whiting to a snail.
" There's a porpoise close behind us, and he's treading
    on my tail.
See how eagerly the lobsters and the turtles all advance!
They are waiting on the shingle—will you come and join
    the dance?
Will you, won't you, will you, won't you, will you join
    the dance?
Will you, won't you, will you, won't you, won't you join
    the dance?

" You can really have no notion how delightful it will be,
When they take us up and throw us, with the lobsters,
    out to sea! "
But the snail replied, " Too far, too far! " and gave a
    look askance—
Said he thanked the whiting kindly, but he would not
    join the dance.

37

Would not, could not, would not, could not, would not
  join the dance.
Would not, could not, would not, could not, could not
  join the dance.

"What matters it how far we go?" his scaly friend
  replied.
"There is another shore, you know, upon the other side.
The further off from England the nearer is to France—
Then turn not pale, belovèd snail, but come and join the
  dance.
Will you, won't you, will you, won't you, will you join
  the dance?
Will you, won't you, will you, won't you, won't you join
  the dance?"

LEWIS CARROLL

GET UP AND BAR THE DOOR

It fell about the Martinmas time,
  And a gay time it was then,
When our goodwife got puddings to make,
  And she's boil'd them in the pan.

The wind sae cauld blew south and north,
  And blew into the floor;
Quoth our goodman to our goodwife,
  "Gae out and bar the door."

"My hand is in my hussyfskep,
  Goodman, as ye may see;
hussyfskep] a bushel basket containing grain, malt, or sugar.

38

An it shou'd nae be barr'd this hundred year,
    It's no be barr'd for me."

They made a paction 'tween them twa,
    They made it firm and sure,
That the first word whae'er shou'd speak
    Shou'd rise and bar the door.

Then by there came twa gentlemen,
    At twelve o'clock at night,
And they cou'd neither see house nor hall,
    Nor coal nor candle-light.

"Now whether is this a rich man's house,
    Or whether it is a poor?"
But ne'er a word wad ane o' them speak,
    For barring of the door.

At first they ate the white puddings,
    And then they ate the black;
Though muckle thought the goodwife to hersel',
    Yet ne'er a word she spake.

Then said the ane unto the other,
    "Here, man, tak ye my knife;
Do ye tak off the auld man's beard,
    And I'll kiss the goodwife."—

"But there's nae water in the house,
    And what shall we do than?"—
"What ails ye at the pudding-broo,
    That boils into the pan?"

O up and started our goodman,
    An angry man was he:
" Will ye kiss my wife before my een,
    And sca'd me wi' pudding-bree? "

Then up and started our goodwife,
    Gied three skips on the floor:
" Goodman, you've spoken the foremost word!
    Get up and bar the door."

ANONYMOUS

YOU ARE OLD, FATHER WILLIAM

" You are old, Father William," the young man said,
    " And your hair has become very white;
And yet you incessantly stand on your head—
    Do you think, at your age, it is right? "

" In my youth," Father William replied to his son,
    " I feared it might injure the brain;
But now that I'm perfectly sure I have none,
    Why, I do it again and again."

" You are old," said the youth, " as I mentioned before,
    And have grown most uncommonly fat;
Yet you turned a back-somersault in at the door—
    Pray, what is the reason of that? "

" In my youth," said the sage, as he shook his grey locks,
    " I kept all my limbs very supple
By the use of this ointment—one shilling the box—
    Allow me to sell you a couple."

40

"You are old," said the youth, "and your jaws are too
weak
  For anything tougher than suet;
Yet you finished the goose, with the bones and the
beak—
  Pray, how did you manage to do it?"

"In my youth," said his father, "I took to the law,
  And argued each case with my wife;
And the muscular strength which it gave to my jaw
  Has lasted the rest of my life."

"You are old," said the youth; "one would hardly
suppose
  That your eye was as steady as ever;
Yet you balanced an eel on the end of your nose—
  What made you so awfully clever?"

"I have answered three questions, and that is enough,"
  Said his father; "don't give yourself airs!
Do you think I can listen all day to such stuff?
  Be off, or I'll kick you down stairs!"

                        LEWIS CARROLL

THE DIVERTING HISTORY OF JOHN GILPIN

*Showing how he went farther than he intended, and
came safe home again*

      John Gilpin was a citizen
      Of credit and renown,
      A train-band captain eke was he
      Of famous London town.

John Gilpin's spouse said to her dear—
" Though wedded we have been
These twice ten tedious years, yet we
No holiday have seen.

" To-morrow is our wedding-day,
And we will then repair
Unto the Bell at Edmonton,
All in a chaise and pair.

" My sister, and my sister's child,
Myself, and children three,
Will fill the chaise; so you must ride
On horseback after we."

He soon replied—" I do admire
Of womankind but one,
And you are she, my dearest dear,
Therefore it shall be done.

" I am a linen-draper bold,
As all the world doth know,
And my good friend the calender
Will lend his horse to go."

Quoth Mrs. Gilpin—" That's well said;
And, for that wine is dear,
We will be furnished with our own,
Which is both bright and clear."

John Gilpin kissed his loving wife;
O'erjoyed was he to find
That, though on pleasure she was bent,
She had a frugal mind.

calender] cloth finisher.

42

The morning came, the chaise was brought,
But yet was not allowed
To drive up to the door, lest all
Should say that she was proud.

So three doors off the chaise was stayed,
Where they did all get in;
Six precious souls, and all agog
To dash through thick and thin!

Smack went the whip, round went the wheels,
Were never folk so glad,
The stones did rattle underneath,
As if Cheapside were mad.

John Gilpin at his horse's side
Seized fast the flowing mane,
And up he got, in haste to ride,
But soon came down again;

For saddle-tree scarce reached had he,
His journey to begin,
When, turning round his head, he saw
Three customers come in.

So down he came; for loss of time,
Although it grieved him sore,
Yet loss of pence, full well he knew,
Would trouble him much more.

'Twas long before the customers
Were suited to their mind,
When Betty screaming came downstairs—
" The wine is left behind! "

"Good lack!" quoth he—"yet bring it me,
My leathern belt likewise,
In which I bear my trusty sword
When I do exercise."

Now mistress Gilpin (careful soul!)
Had two stone bottles found,
To hold the liquor that she loved,
And keep it safe and sound.

Each bottle had a curling ear,
Through which the belt he drew,
And hung a bottle on each side,
To make his balance true.

Then, over all, that he might be
Equipped from top to toe,
His long red cloak, well brushed and neat,
He manfully did throw.

Now see him mounted once again
Upon his nimble steed,
Full slowly pacing o'er the stones
With caution and good heed!

But, finding soon a smoother road
Beneath his well-shod feet,
The snorting beast began to trot,
Which galled him in his seat.

So, "Fair and softly," John he cried,
But John he cried in vain;
That trot became a gallop soon,
In spite of curb and rein.

So stooping down, as needs he must
Who cannot sit upright,
He grasped the mane with both his hands,
And eke with all his might.

His horse, who never in that sort
Had handled been before,
What thing upon his back had got
Did wonder more and more.

Away went Gilpin, neck or nought;
Away went hat and wig!—
He little dreamt, when he set out,
Of running such a rig!

The wind did blow, the cloak did fly
Like streamer long and gay,
Till, loop and button failing both,
At last it flew away.

Then might all people well discern
The bottles he had slung;
A bottle swinging at each side,
As hath been said or sung.

The dogs did bark, the children screamed,
Up flew the windows all;
And ev'ry soul cried out—" Well done! "
As loud as he could bawl.

Away went Gilpin—who but he?
His fame soon spread around—
" He carries weight! " " He rides a race! "
" 'Tis for a thousand pound! "

And still, as fast as he drew near,
'Twas wonderful to view
How in a trice the turnpike-men
Their gates wide open threw.

And now, as he went bowing down
His reeking head full low,
The bottles twain behind his back
Were shattered at a blow.

Down ran the wine into the road,
Most piteous to be seen,
Which made his horse's flanks to smoke
As they had basted been.

But still he seemed to carry weight,
With leathern girdle braced;
For all might see the bottle-necks
Still dangling at his waist.

Thus all through merry Islington
These gambols he did play,
Until he came unto the Wash
Of Edmonton so gay.

And there he threw the wash about
On both sides of the way,
Just like unto a trundling mop,
Or a wild goose at play.

Wash] a low-lying stretch of land.
wash] pools of water lying on the marshy ground.

At Edmonton his loving wife
From the balcóny spied
Her tender husband, wond'ring much
To see how he did ride.

"Stop, stop, John Gilpin!—Here's the house"—
They all at once did cry;
"The dinner waits, and we are tired."
Said Gilpin—"So am I!"

But yet his horse was not a whit
Inclined to tarry there;
For why?—his owner had a house
Full ten miles off, at Ware.

So like an arrow swift he flew,
Shot by an archer strong;
So did he fly—which brings me to
The middle of my song.

Away went Gilpin, out of breath,
And sore against his will,
Till at his friend the calender's
His horse at last stood still.

The calender, amazed to see
His neighbour in such trim,
Laid down his pipe, flew to the gate,
And thus accosted him:—

"What news? what news? your tidings tell;
Tell me you must and shall—
Say why bare-headed you are come,
Or why you come at all?"

Now Gilpin had a pleasant wit,
And loved a timely joke;
And thus unto the calender
In merry guise he spoke:—

"I came because your horse would come;
And, if I well forebode,
My hat and wig will soon be here—
They are upon the road."

The calender, right glad to find
His friend in merry pin,
Returned him not a single word,
But to the house went in;

Whence straight he came with hat and wig;
A wig that flowed behind,
A hat not much the worse for wear,
Each comely in its kind.

He held them up, and, in his turn,
Thus showed his ready wit—
"My head is twice as big as yours,
They therefore needs must fit.

"But let me scrape the dirt away
That hangs upon your face;
And stop and eat, for well you may
Be in a hungry case."

Said John—"It is my wedding-day,
And all the world would stare,
If wife should dine at Edmonton
And I should dine at Ware!"

So, turning to his horse, he said—
" I am in haste to dine;
'Twas for your pleasure you came here,
You shall go back for mine."

Ah, luckless speech, and bootless boast!
For which he paid full dear;
For, while he spake, a braying ass
Did sing most loud and clear;

Whereat his horse did snort, as he
Had heard a lion roar,
And galloped off with all his might,
As he had done before.

Away went Gilpin, and away
Went Gilpin's hat and wig!
He lost them sooner than at first—
For why?—they were too big!

Now, mistress Gilpin, when she saw
Her husband posting down
Into the country far away,
She pulled out half a crown;

And thus unto the youth she said
That drove them to the Bell—
" This shall be yours when you bring back
My husband safe and well."

The youth did ride, and soon did meet
John coming back amain;
Whom in a trice he tried to stop,
By catching at his rein;

49

But, not performing what he meant,
And gladly would have done,
The frighted steed he frighted more,
And made him faster run.

Away went Gilpin, and away
Went post-boy at his heels!—
The post-boy's horse right glad to miss
The lumb'ring of the wheels.

Six gentlemen upon the road,
Thus seeing Gilpin fly,
With post-boy scamp'ring in the rear,
They raised the hue and cry:

"Stop thief! stop thief!—a highwayman!"
Not one of them was mute;
And all and each that passed that way
Did join in the pursuit.

And now the turnpike gates again
Flew open in short space;
The toll-men thinking, as before,
That Gilpin rode a race.

And so he did—and won it too!—
For he got first to town;
Nor stopped till where he had got up
He did again get down.

Now let us sing—Long live the king,
And Gilpin long live he;
And, when he next doth ride abroad,
May I be there to see!

WILLIAM COWPER

THE WONDERFUL "ONE-HOSS SHAY"

Have you heard of the wonderful One-Hoss Shay,
That was built in such a logical way
It ran a hundred years to a day?
And then of a sudden it—ah! but stay,
I'll tell you what happened, without delay—
Scaring the parson into fits,
Frightening people out of their wits—
Have you ever heard of that, I say?

Seventeen hundred and fifty-five;
Georgius Secundus was then alive—
Snuffy old drone from the German hive!—
That was the year when Lisbon town
Saw the earth open and gulp her down;
And Braddock's army was done so brown,
Left without a scalp to its crown.
It was on that terrible Earthquake day
That the Deacon finished the One-Hoss Shay.

Now, in building of chaises, I tell you what,
There is always, *somewhere*, a weakest spot—
In hub, tire, felloe, in spring or thill,
In panel or crossbar, or floor, or sill,
In screw, bolt, thorough-brace—lurking still.
Find it somewhere, you must and will—
Above or below, or within or without—
And that's the reason, beyond a doubt,
A chaise *breaks down*, but doesn't *wear out.*

51

But the Deacon swore (as deacons do,
With an " I dew vum " or an " I tell yeou,")
He would build one shay to beat the taown
'N' the keounty 'n' the kentry raoun ";
It should be built so that it couldn' break daown :
" Fur," said the Deacon, " 'tis mighty plain
Thut the weakes' place mus' stan' the strain;
'N' the way t' fix it, uz I maintain,
            Is only jest
To make that place uz strong uz the rest."

So the Deacon inquired of the village folk
Where he could find the strongest oak,
That couldn't be split, nor bent, nor broke—
That was for spokes and floor and sills;
He sent for lancewood to make the thills;
The crossbars were ash, from the straightest trees;
The panels of white-wood, that cuts like cheese,
But lasts like iron for things like these;
The hubs from logs from the " Settler's Ellum,"
Last of its timber—they couldn't sell 'em—
Never an axe had seen their chips,
And the wedges flew from between their lips,
Their blunt ends frizzled like celery-tips;
Step and prop-iron, bolt and screw,
Spring, hide, axle, and linch-pin too,
Steel of the finest, bright and blue;
Thorough-brace bison-skin, thick and wide;
Boot, top, dasher, from tough old hide,
Found in the pit where the tanner died.
That was the way he " put her through."
" There," said the Deacon, " naow she'll dew ! "

Do! I tell you, I rather guess
She was a wonder, and nothing less!
Colts grew horses, beards turned grey,
Deacon and deaconess dropped away;
Children and grandchildren—where were they?
But there stood the stout old One-Hoss Shay,
As fresh as on Lisbon Earthquake day!

Eighteen hundred—it came, and found
The Deacon's masterpiece strong and sound.
Eighteen hundred, increased by ten—
" Hahnsum Kerridge " they called it then.
Eighteen hundred and twenty came—
Running as usual—much the same.
Thirty and *forty* at last arrive;
And then came *fifty*—and *fifty-five*.

Little of all we value here
Wakes on the morn of its hundredth year
Without both feeling and looking queer.
In fact, there's nothing that keeps its youth,
So far as I know, but a tree and truth.
(This is a moral that runs at large;
Take it—you're welcome—no extra charge.)

First of November—the Earthquake day—
There are traces of age in the One-Hoss Shay—
A general flavour of mild decay—
But nothing local, as one may say.
There couldn't be, for the Deacon's art
Had made it so like in every part
That there wasn't a chance for one to start.
For the wheels were just as strong as the thills,

53

And the floor was just as strong as the sills,
And the panels just as strong as the floor,
And the whipple-tree neither less nor more,
And the back crossbar as strong as the fore,
And the spring and axle and hub *encore*;
And yet, *as a whole*, it is past a doubt,
In another hour it will be *worn out*!

First of November, 'Fifty-five!
This morning the parson takes a drive.
Now, small boys, get out of the way!
Here comes the wonderful One-hoss Shay,
Drawn by a rat-tailed, ewe-necked bay.
"Huddup!" said the parson—off went they!

The parson was working his Sunday's text;
Had got to *fifthly*, and stopped, perplexed
At what the—Moses—was coming next.
All at once the horse stood still,
Close by the meet'n'-house on the hill:
—First a shiver, and then a thrill;
And something decidedly like a spill;
And the parson was sitting upon a rock,
At half-past nine by the meet'n'-house clock—
Just the hour of the Earthquake shock!
What do you think the parson found
When he got up and stared around?
The poor old chaise in a heap or mound,
As if it had been to the mill and ground;
You see, of course, if you're not a dunce,
How it went to pieces all at once—
All at once, and nothing first—
Just as bubbles do when they burst.

End of the wonderful One-Hoss Shay!
Logic is *Logic*—that's all I say.

OLIVER WENDELL HOLMES

THE OLD NAVY

The captain stood on the carronade: "First lieutenant,"
    says he,
" Send all my merry men aft here, for they must list to
    me;
I haven't the gift of the gab, my sons—because I'm bred
    to the sea;
That ship there is a Frenchman, who means to fight with
    we.
        And odds bobs, hammer and tongs, long as I've
            been to sea,
        I've fought 'gainst every odds—and I've gained
            the victory!

" That ship there is a Frenchman, and if we don't take
    she,
'Tis a thousand bullets to one, that she will capture we;
I haven't the gift of the gab, my boys; so each man to
    his gun;
If she's not mine in half an hour, I'll flog each mother's
    son.
        For odds bobs, hammer and tongs, long as I've
            been to sea,
        I've fought 'gainst every odds—and I've gained
            the victory! "

carronade] naval gun first cast at Carron, near Edinburgh.

55

We fought for twenty minutes, when the Frenchman
    had enough;
" I little thought," said he, " that your men were of such
    stuff ":
Our captain took the Frenchman's sword, a low bow
    made to he;
" I haven't the gift of the gab, monsieur, but polite I
    wish to be.

      And odds bobs, hammer and tongs, long as I've
        been to sea,
      I've fought 'gainst every odds—and I've gained
        the victory! "

Our captain sent for all of us: " My merry men," said
    he,
" I haven't the gift of the gab, my lads, but yet I thankful
    be:
You've done your duty handsomely, each man stood to
    his gun;
If you hadn't, you villains, as sure as day, I'd have
    flogged each mother's son,
      For odds bobs, hammer and tongs, as long as I'm
        at sea,
      I'll fight 'gainst every odds—and I'll gain the
        victory! "

FREDERICK MARRYAT

TARANTELLA

Do you remember an Inn,
Miranda?
Do you remember an Inn?

And the tedding and the spreading
Of the straw for a bedding,
And the fleas that tease in the High Pyrenees,
And the wine that tasted of the tar?
And the cheers and the jeers of the young muleteers
(Under the vine of the dark verandah)?
Do you remember an Inn, Miranda,
Do you remember an Inn?
And the cheers and the jeers of the young muleteers
Who hadn't got a penny,
And who weren't paying any,
And the hammer at the doors and the Din?
And the Hip! Hop! Hap!
Of the clap
Of the hands to the twirl and the swirl
Of the girl gone chancing,
Glancing,
Dancing,
Backing and advancing,
Snapping of the clapper to the spin
Out and in——
And the Ting, Tong, Tang of the Guitar!
Do you remember an Inn,
Miranda?
Do you remember an Inn?

    Never more,
    Miranda,
    Never more.
    Only the high peaks hoar:
    And Aragon a torrent at the door.
    No sound

In the walls of the Halls where falls
The tread
Of the feet of the dead to the ground,
No sound:
But the boom
Of the far Waterfall like Doom.

HILAIRE BELLOC

THE PARROT

The old professor of Zoology
Shook his long beard and spake these words to me:
" Compare the Parrot with the Dove. They are
In shape the same: in hue dissimilar.
The Indian bird, which may be sometimes seen
In red or black, is generally green.
His beak is very hard: it has been known
To crack thick nuts and penetrate a stone.
Alas that when you teach him how to speak
You find his head is harder than his beak.

" The passionless Malay can safely drub
The pates of parrots with an iron club:
The ingenious fowls, like boys they beat at school,
Soon learn to recognize a Despot's rule.
    Now if you'd train a parrot, catch him young
While soft the mouth and tractable the tongue.
Old birds are fools: they dodder in their speech,
More eager to forget than you to teach;
They swear one curse, then gaze at you askance,
And all oblivion thickens in their glance.

58

" Thrice blest whose parrot of his own accord
Invents new phrases to delight his Lord,
Who spurns the dull quotidian task and tries
Selected words that prove him good and wise.
Ah, once it was my privilege to know
A bird like this . . .
                    But that was long ago! "
                                        JAMES ELROY FLECKER

ON A FAVOURITE CAT

DROWNED IN A TUB OF GOLD FISHES

'Twas on a lofty vase's side,
Where China's gayest art had dyed
    The azure flowers that blow;
Demurest of the Tabby kind,
The pensive Selima reclin'd,
    Gaz'd on the lake below.

Her conscious tail her joy declar'd;
The fair round face, the snowy beard,
    The velvet of her paws,
Her coat, that with the tortoise vies,
Her ears of jet, and emerald eyes,
    She saw; and purr'd applause.

Still had she gaz'd: but 'midst the tide
Two angel forms were seen to glide,
    The Genii of the stream;
Their scaly armour's Tyrian hue
Through richest purple, to the view
    Betray'd a golden gleam.

The hapless Nymph with wonder saw:
A whisker first, and then a claw,
  With many an ardent wish,
She stretch'd in vain to reach the prize.
What female heart can gold despise?
  What Cat's averse to fish?

Presumptuous Maid! with looks intent
Again she stretch'd, again she bent,
  Nor knew the gulph between.
(Malignant Fate sat by, and smil'd.)
The slipp'ry verge her feet beguil'd,
  She tumbled headlong in.

Eight times emerging from the flood
She mew'd to ev'ry wat'ry god,
  Some speedy aid to send.
No Dolphin came, no Nereid stirr'd:
Nor cruel Tom, nor Susan heard.
  A Fav'rite has no friend!

From hence, ye Beauties undeceiv'd,
Know, one false step is ne'er retriev'd,
  And be with caution bold.
Not all that tempts your wand'ring eyes
And heedless hearts, is lawful prize;
  Nor all that glisters, gold.

THOMAS GRAY

THE TOWN MOUSE AND THE COUNTRY MOUSE

From " Imitations of Horace "

Once on a time, so runs the fable,
A country mouse, right hospitable,
Received a town mouse at his board,
Just as a farmer might a lord.
A frugal mouse, upon the whole,
Yet loved his friend, and had a soul,
Knew what was handsome, and could do't,
On just occasion, " coûte que coûte."
He brought him bacon, nothing lean,
Pudding, that might have pleased a Dean;
Cheese, such as men in Suffolk make,
But wish'd it Stilton for his sake;
Yet, to his guest though no way sparing,
He ate himself the rind and paring.
Our courtier scarce could touch a bit,
But showed his breeding and his wit;
He did his best to seem to eat,
And cried, " I vow, you're mighty neat.
But Lord, my friend, this savage scene !
For God's sake, come and live with men :
Consider, mice, like men, must die,
Both small and great, both you and I;
Then spend your life in joy and sport,
(This doctrine, friend, I learnt at court)."
The veriest hermit in the nation,
May yield, God knows, to strong temptation.
Away they come, through thick and thin,

To a tall house near Lincoln's Inn:
('Twas on the night of a debate,
When all their Lordships had sat late.)
  Behold the place, where if a poet
Shined in description, he might show it;
Tell how the moon-beam trembling falls,
And tips with silver all the walls;
Palladian walls, Venetian doors,
Grotesco roofs, and stucco floors:
But let it, in a word, be said,
The moon was up, and men a-bed,
The napkins white, the carpet red:
The guests withdrawn had left the treat.
And down the mice sat, tête-à-tête.
  Our courtier walks from dish to dish,
Tastes for his friend of fowl and fish;
Tells all their names, lays down the law,
" Que ça est bon! Ah, goutez ça!
That jelly's rich, this Malmsey healing,
Pray dip your whiskers and your tail in."
Was ever such a happy swain?
He stuffs, and swills, and stuffs again.
" I'm quite asham'd—'tis mighty rude
To eat so much—but all's so good.
I've a thousand thanks to give—
My Lord alone knows how to live."
No sooner said, than from the hall
Rush chaplain, butler, dogs and all:
" A rat, a rat! clap to the door "—
The cat comes bouncing on the floor.
O for the heart of Homer's mice,
Or gods to save them in a trice!

It was by Providence, they think,
For your damned stucco has no chink.
" An't please your honour," quoth the peasant,
" This same dessert is not so pleasant:
Give me again my hollow tree,
A crust of bread, and liberty! "

ALEXANDER POPE

NARRATIVE POEMS

THE THREE BEGGARS

'Twas autumn daybreak gold and wild
   While past St. Ann's grey tower they shuffled
Three beggars spied a fairy-child
   In crimson mantle muffled.

The daybreak lighted up her face
   All pink, and sharp, and emerald-eyed;
She looked on them a little space,
   And shrill as hautboy cried:—

" O three tall footsore men in rags
   Which walking this gold moon I see,
What will ye give me from your bags
   For fairy kisses three? "

The first that was a reddish man,
   Out of his bundle takes a crust:
" La, by the tombstones of St. Ann
   There's fee, if fee ye must! "

The second, that was a chestnut man,
   Out of his bundle draws a bone:
" La, by the belfry of St. Ann,
   And all my breakfast gone! "

The third, that was a yellow man,
　Out of his bundle picks a groat,
"La, the Angel of St. Ann,
　And I must go without."

That changeling, lean and icy-lipped,
　Touched crust, and bone, and groat, and lo!
Beneath her finger taper-tipped
　The magic all ran through.

Instead of crust a peacock pie,
　Instead of bone sweet venison,
Instead of groat a white lily
　With seven blooms thereon.

And each fair cup was deep with wine:
　Such was the changeling's charity
The sweet feast was enough for nine,
　But not too much for three.

O toothsome meat in jelly froze;
　O tender haunch of elfin stag;
Oh, rich the odour that arose!
　Oh, plump with scraps each bag!

There, in the daybreak gold and wild,
　Each merry-hearted beggar man
Drank deep unto the fairy child,
　And blessed the good St. Ann.

                              WALTER DE LA MARE

THE FORSAKEN MERMAN

Come, dear children, let us away:
   Down and away below!
Now my brothers call from the bay;
   Now the great winds shorewards blow;
   Now the salt tides seawards flow;
Now the wild white horses play,
Champ and chafe and toss in the spray.
Children dear, let us away!
   This way, this way!

Call her once before you go.
   Call once yet.
In a voice that she will know:
   "Margaret! Margaret!"
Children's voices should be dear
(Call once more) to a mother's ear:
Children's voices, wild with pain—
Surely she will come again.
Call her once and come away;
   This way, this way!
"Mother dear, we cannot stay."
The wild white horses foam and fret.
   Margaret! Margaret!

Come, dear children, come away down!
   Call no more!
One last look at the white-walled town,
And the little grey church on the windy shore.
   Then come down.
She will not come though you call all day.
   Come away, come away!

67

Children dear, was it yesterday
We heard the sweet bells over the bay
In the caverns where we lay,
Through the surf and through the swell,
The far-off sound of a silver bell?
Sand-strewn caverns, cool and deep,
Where the winds are all asleep;
Where the spent lights quiver and gleam;
Where the salt weed sways in the stream;
Where the sea-beasts ranged all round
Feed in the ooze of their pasture-ground;
Where the sea-snakes coil and twine,
Dry their mail and bask in the brine;
Where great whales come sailing by,
Sail and sail, with unshut eye,
Round the world for ever and aye?
When did music come this way?
Children dear, was it yesterday?

Children dear, was it yesterday
(Call yet once) that she went away?
Once she sate with you and me,
On a red gold throne in the heart of the sea,
And the youngest sate on her knee.
She comb'd its bright hair, and she tended it well,
When down swung the sound of the far-off bell.
She sigh'd, she look'd up through the clear green sea;
She said: "I must go, for my kinsfolk pray
In the little grey church on the shore to-day.
'Twill be Easter-time in the world—ah me!
And I lose my poor soul, Merman, here with thee."
I said: "Go up, dear heart, through the waves!

68

Say thy prayer, and come back to the kind sea-caves."
She smiled, she went up through the surf in the bay.
Children dear, was it yesterday?

 Children dear, were we long alone?
" The sea grows stormy, the little ones moan.
Long prayers," I said, " in the world they say.
Come! " I said, and we rose through the surf in the
     bay.
We went up the beach, by the sandy down
Where the sea-stocks bloom, to the white-walled town.
Through the narrow paved streets, where all was still,
To the little grey church on the windy hill.
From the church came a murmur of folk at their
     prayers,
But we stood without in the cold blowing airs.
We climbed on the graves, on the stones, worn with
     rains,
And we gazed up the aisle through the small leaded
     panes.
She sate by the pillar; we saw her clear:
" Margaret, hist! come quick, we are here.
Dear heart," I said, " we are long alone.
The sea grows stormy, the little ones moan."
But, ah, she gave me never a look,
For her eyes were sealed to the holy book!
Loud prays the priest; shut stands the door.
Come away, children, call no more!
Come away, come down, call no more!

 Down, down, down!
 Down to the depths of the sea!

She sits at her wheel in the humming town,
   Singing most joyfully.
Hark, what she sings: "O joy, O joy,
For the humming street, and the child with its toy!
For the priest, and the bell, and the holy well—
   For the wheel where I spun,
   And the blessed light of the sun!"
   And so she sings her fill,
   Singing most joyfully,
Till the shuttle falls from her hand,
   And the whizzing wheel stands still.
She steals to the window, and looks at the sand,
   And over the sand at the sea;
And her eyes are set in a stare;
   And anon there breaks a sigh,
And anon there drops a tear,
   From a sorrow-clouded eye,
And a heart sorrow-laden,
   A long, long sigh,
For the cold strange eyes of a little Mermaiden
   And the gleam of her golden hair.

Come away, away children!
   Come children, come down!
The hoarse wind blows colder;
   Lights shine in the town.
She will start from her slumber
   When gusts shake the door;
She will hear the winds howling,
   Will hear the waves roar.
We shall see, while above us
   The waves roar and whirl,

A ceiling of amber,
　　A pavement of pearl.
Singing: " Here came a mortal,
　　But faithless was she!
And alone dwell for ever
　　The kings of the sea."

But, children, at midnight,
　　When soft the winds blow,
When clear falls the moonlight,
　　When spring-tides are low;
When sweet airs come seaward
　　From heaths starred with broom,
And high rocks throw mildly
　　On the blanched sands a gloom;
Up the still, glistening beaches,
　　Up the creeks we will hie,
Over banks of bright seaweed
　　The ebb-tide leaves dry,
We will gaze, from the sand-hills,
　　At the white, sleeping town;
At the church on the hill-side—
　　And then come back down.
Singing: " There dwells a loved one,
　　But cruel is she!
She left lonely for ever
　　The kings of the sea."

MATTHEW ARNOLD

71

A RUNNABLE STAG

When the pods went pop on the broom, green broom,
   And apples began to be golden-skinned,
We harboured a stag in the Priory coomb,
   And we feathered his trail up-wind, up-wind,
   We feathered his trail up-wind—
      A stag of warrant, a stag, a stag,
      A runnable stag, a kingly crop,
      Brow, bay and tray and three on top,
      A stag, a runnable stag.

Then the huntsman's horn rang yap, yap, yap,
   And "Forwards" we heard the harbourer shout,
But 'twas only a brocket that broke a gap
   In the beechen underwood, driven out,
   From the underwood antlered out
      By warrant and might of the stag, the stag,
      The runnable stag, whose lordly mind
      Was bent on sleep, though beamed and tined
      He stood, a runnable stag.

So we tufted the covert till afternoon
   With Tinkerman's Pup and Bell-of-the-North;
And hunters were sulky and hounds out of tune
   Before we tufted the right stag forth,
   Before we tufted him forth,

harboured] tracked to his lair.   coomb] a deep, narrow valley.
   brow, bay and tray] the first, second, and third antlers.
   brocket] a young stag with only its first horns.
beam] is the main trunk of a stag's horn; it bears the antlers.
tines] are the pointed branches of a stag's horn.

The stag of warrant, the wily stag,
The runnable stag with his kingly crop,
Brow, bay and tray and three on top,
The royal and runnable stag.

It was Bell-of-the-North and Tinkerman's Pup
  That stuck to the scent till the copse was drawn.
"Tally ho! tally ho!" and the hunt was up,
  The tufters whipped and the pack laid on,
    The resolute pack laid on,
      And the stag of warrant away at last,
      The runnable stag, the same, the same,
      His hoofs on fire, his horns like flame,
      A stag, a runnable stag.

"Let your gelding be: if you check or chide
  He stumbles at once and you're out of the hunt;
For three hundred gentlemen, able to ride,
  On hunters accustomed to bear the brunt,
    Accustomed to bear the brunt,
      Are after the runnable stag, the stag,
      The runnable stag with his kingly crop,
      Brow, bay and tray and three on top,
      The right, the runnable stag.

By perilous paths in coomb and dell,
  The heather, the rocks, and the river-bed,
The pace grew hot, for the scent lay well,
  And a runnable stag goes right ahead,
    The quarry went right ahead—
      Ahead, ahead, and fast and far;
      His antlered crest, his cloven hoof,
      Brow, bay and tray and three aloof,
      The stag, the runnable stag.

c*

For a matter of twenty miles and more,
  By the densest hedge and the highest wall,
Through herds of bullocks he baffled the lore
  Of harbourer, huntsman, hounds and all,
  Of harbourer, hounds and all—
    The stag of warrant, the wily stag,
    For twenty miles, and five and five,
    He ran, and he never was caught alive,
    This stag, this runnable stag.

When he turned at bay in the leafy gloom,
  In the emerald gloom where the brook ran deep
He heard in the distance the rollers boom,
  And he saw in a vision of peaceful sleep,
  In a wonderful vision of sleep,
    A stag of warrant, a stag, a stag,
    A runnable stag in a jewelled bed,
    Under the sheltering ocean dead,
    A stag, a runnable stag.

So a fateful hope lit up his eye,
  And he opened his nostrils wide again,
And he tossed his branching antlers high
  As he headed the hunt down the Charlock glen
  As he raced down the echoing glen
    For five miles more, the stag, the stag,
    For twenty miles, and five and five,
    Not to be caught now, dead or alive,
    The stag, the runnable stag.

Three hundred gentlemen, able to ride,
  Three hundred horses as gallant and free,

Beheld him escape on the evening tide,
Far out till he sank in the Severn Sea,
Till he sank in the depths of the sea—
The stag, the buoyant stag, the stag
That slept at last in a jewelled bed
Under the sheltering ocean spread,
The stag, the runnable stag.

JOHN DAVIDSON

AGINCOURT

Fair stood the wind for France,
When we our sails advance,
Nor now to prove our chance
　Longer will tarry;
But putting to the main,
At Caux, the mouth of Seine,
With all his martial train,
　Landed King Harry.

And taking many a fort,
Furnish'd in warlike sort,
Marcheth towards Agincourt
　In happy hour;
Skirmishing day by day
With those that stopp'd his way,
Where the French general lay
　With all his power.

Which, in his height of pride,
King Henry to deride,
His ransom to provide
　Unto him sending;

75

Which he neglects the while
As from a nation vile,
Yet with an angry smile
  Their fall portending.

And turning to his men,
Quoth our brave Henry then,
"Though they to one be ten
  Be not amazèd:
Yet have we well begun;
Battles so bravely won
Have ever to the sun
  By fame been raisèd.

"And for myself" (quoth he):
This my full rest shall be:
England ne'er mourn for me
  Nor more esteem me:
Victor I will remain
Or on this earth lie slain,
Never shall she sustain
  Loss to redeem me.

"Poitiers and Cressy tell,
When most their pride did swell,
Under our swords they fell:
  No less our skill is
Than when our grandsire great,
Claiming the regal seat,
By many a warlike feat
  Lopp'd the French lilies."

The Duke of York so dread
The eager vaward led;

With the main Henry sped
  Amongst his henchmen.
Excester had the rear,
A braver man not there;
O Lord, how hot they were
  On the false Frenchmen!

They now to fight are gone,
Armour on armour shone,
Drum now to drum did groan,
  To hear was wonder;
That with the cries they make
The very earth did shake:
Trumpet to trumpet spake,
  Thunder to thunder.

Well it thine age became,
O noble Erpingham,
Which didst the signal aim
  To our hid forces!
When from a meadow by,
Like a storm suddenly
The English archery
  Stuck the French horses.

With Spanish yew so strong,
Arrows a cloth-yard long
That like to serpents stung,
  Piercing the weather;
None from his fellow starts,
But playing manly parts,
And like true English hearts
  Stuck close together.

77

When down their bows they threw,
And forth their bilbos drew,
And on the French they flew,
    Not one was tardy;
Arms were from shoulders sent,
Scalps to the teeth were rent,
Down the French peasants went—
    Our men were hardy.

This while our noble king,
His broadsword brandishing,
Down the French host did ding
    As to o'erwhelm it;
And many a deep wound lent,
His arms with blood besprent,
And many a cruel dent
    Bruisèd his helmet.

Gloster, that duke so good,
Next of the royal blood,
For famous England stood
    With his brave brother;
Clarence, in steel so bright,
Though but a maiden knight,
Yet in that furious fight
    Scarce such another.

Warwick in blood did wade,
Oxford the foe invade,
And cruel slaughter made
    Still as they ran up;

bilbos] swords.   ding] beat down with resounding blows

78

Suffolk his axe did ply,
Beaumont and Willoughby
Bare them right doughtily,
   Ferrers and Fanhope.

Upon Saint Crispin's Day
Fought was this noble fray,
Which fame did not delay
   To England to carry.
O when shall English men
With such acts fill a pen?
Or England breed again
   Such a King Harry?

MICHAEL DRAYTON

SINGING LEAVES

I

"What fairings will ye that I bring?"
   Said the King to his daughters three;
"For I to Vanity Fair am bound,
   Now say what shall they be?"

Then up and spake the eldest daughter,
   That lady tall and grand:
"Oh, bring me pearls and diamonds great,
   And gold rings for my hand."

Thereafter spake the second daughter,
   That was both white and red;
"For me bring silks that will stand alone,
   And a gold comb for my head."

79

Then came the turn of the least daughter,
    That was whiter than thistle-down,
And among the gold of her blithesome hair
    Dim shone the golden crown.

" There came a bird this morning,
    And sang 'neath my bower eaves,
Till I dreamed, as his music made me,
    ' Ask thou for the Singing Leaves.' "

Then the brow of the King swelled crimson
    With a flush of angry scorn:
" Well have ye spoken, my two eldest,
    And chosen as ye were born;

" But she, like a thing of peasant race,
    That is happy binding the sheaves ";
Then he saw her dead mother in her face,
    And said, " Thou shalt have thy leaves."

II

He mounted and rode three days and nights,
    Till he came to Vanity Fair,
And 'twas easy to buy the gems and the silk,
    But no Singing Leaves were there.

Then deep in the greenwood rode he,
    And asked of every tree,
" Oh, if you have a Singing Leaf,
    I pray you give it me! "

But the trees all kept their counsel,
    And never a word said they,
Only there sighed from the pine-tops
    A music of seas far away.

Only the faltering aspen
    Made a sound of growing rain,
That fell ever faster and faster,
    Then faltered to silence again.

" Oh, where shall I find a little foot-page
    That would win both hose and shoon,
And will bring to me the Singing Leaves,
    If they grow under the moon? "

Then lightly turned him Walter the page,
    By the stirrup as he ran:
" Now pledge you me the truesome word
    Of a King and a gentleman,

" That you will give me the first, first thing
    You meet at your castle-gate,
And the princess shall get the Singing Leaves,
    Or mine be a traitor's fate."

The King's head dropped upon his breast
    A moment as it might be;
" 'Twill be my dog," he thought, and said,
    " My faith I plight to thee."

Then Walter took from next his heart
    A packet small and thin,
" Now give you this to the Princess Anne,
    The Singing Leaves are therein."

III

As the King rode in at his castle-gate
    A maiden to meet him ran,
And, " Welcome, father! " she laughed and cried
    Together, the Princess Anne.

"Lo, here the Singing Leaves," quoth he,
  "And woe, but they cost me dear!"
She took the packet, and the smile
  Deepened down beneath the tear.

It deepened down till it reached her heart,
  And then gushed up again,
And lighted her tears as the sudden sun
  Transfigures the summer rain.

And the first Leaf, when it was opened,
  Sang: "I am Walter the page,
And the songs I sing 'neath thy window
  Are my only heritage."

And the second Leaf sang: "But in the land
  That is neither on earth nor sea,
My lute and I are lords of more
  Than thrice this kingdom's fee."

And the third Leaf sang, "Be mine! Be mine!"
  And ever it sang "Be mine!"
Then sweeter it sang, and ever sweeter,
  And said, "I am thine, thine, thine!"

At the first Leaf she grew pale enough,
  At the second she turned aside,
At the third 'twas as if a lily flushed
  With a rose's red heart's tide.

"Good counsel gave the bird," said she,
  "I have my hope thrice o'er,
For they sing to my very heart," she said,
  "And it sings to them ever more."

She brought to him her beauty and truth,
  Birth and broad earldoms three,
And he made her Queen of the broader lands
  He held of his lute in fee.

JAMES RUSSELL LOWELL

THE BALLAD OF FATHER GILLIGAN

The old priest, Peter Gilligan,
  Was weary night and day,
For half his flock were in their beds,
  Or under green sods lay.

Once, while he nodded on a chair,
  At the moth hour of eve,
Another poor man sent for him,
  And he began to grieve.

" I have no rest, nor joy, nor peace,
  For people die and die ";
And after, cried he, " God forgive!
  My body spake, not I! "

He knelt, and leaning on the chair,
  He prayed and fell asleep;
And the moth hour went from the fields,
  And stars began to peep.

They slowly into millions grew,
  And leaves shook in the wind;

moth hour] twilight.

83

And God covered the world with shade,
  And whispered to mankind.

Upon the time of sparrow chirp,
  When the moths came once more,
The old priest Peter Gilligan
  Stood upright on the floor.

"Mavrone, Mavrone! the man has died
  While I slept on the chair";
He roused his horse out of its sleep
  And rode with little care.

He rode now as he never rode,
  By rocky lane and fen;
The sick man's wife opened the door:
  "Father! you come again!"

"And is the poor man dead?" he cried,
  "He died an hour ago."
The old Priest Peter Gilligan
  In grief swayed to and fro.

"When you were gone, he turned and died
  As merry as a bird."
The old priest Peter Gilligan
  He knelt him at that word.

"He who hath made the night of stars,
  For souls who tire and bleed,
Sent one of His great angels down
  To help me in my need.

Mavrone] little mother (The Virgin Mary).

84

" He who is wrapped in purple robes,
  With planets in His care,
Had pity on the least of things
  Asleep upon a chair."

WILLIAM BUTLER YEATS

THE BALLAD OF DICK TURPIN

I

The daylight moon looked quietly down
Through the gathering dusk on London town.

A smock-frockt yokel hobbled along
By Newgate, humming a country song.

Chewing a straw, he stood to stare
At the proclamation posted there:

Three hundred guineas on Turpin's head,
Trap him alive or shoot him dead;
And a hundred more for his mate, Tom King.

He crouched, like a tiger about to spring.

Then he looked up, and he looked down;
And, chuckling low, like a country clown,

Dick Turpin painfully hobbled away
In quest of his Inn—*The Load of Hay.*

. . . . . .

Alone in her stall, his mare, Black Bess,
Lifted her head in mute distress;

For five strange men had entered the yard
And looked at her long, and looked at her hard.

They went out, muttering under their breath:
And then—the dusk grew still as death.

But the velvet ears of the listening mare
Lifted and twitched. *They were there—still there;*

Hidden and waiting; for whom? And why?
The clock struck four. A step drew nigh.

It was King! Tom King! Dick Turpin's mate.
The black mare whinneyed. Too late! Too late!

They rose like shadows out of the ground
And grappled him there, without a sound.

"Throttle him—quietly—choke him dead!
Or we lose the hawk for a jay," they said.

They wrestled and heaved, five men to one;
And a yokel entered the yard, alone;

A smock-frockt yokel, hobbling slow;
But a fight is physic, as all men know.

His age dropped off. He stood upright.
He leapt like a tiger into the fight.

Hand to hand, they fought in the dark;
For none could fire at a twisting mark,

Where he that shot at a foe might send
His pistol-ball through the skull of a friend.

But *"Shoot, Dick, shoot!"* gasped out Tom King.
"Shoot, or damn it, we both shall swing!

86

Shoot and chance it!" Dick leapt back.
He drew. He fired. At the pistol's crack

The wrestlers whirled. They scattered apart,
And the bullet drilled through Tom King's heart.

.   .   .   .   .

Dick Turpin dropped his smoking gun.
They had trapped him now, five men to one.

A gun in each hand of the crouching five,
They could take Dick Turpin now, alive;

Take him and bind him and tell their tale
As a pot-house boast, when they drank their ale.

He whistled, soft as a bird might call;
And a head-rope snapped in his bird's dark stall.

He whistled, soft as a nightingale.
He heard the swish of her swinging tail.

There was no way out that the five could see,
To heaven or hell, but the Tyburn tree;

No door but death; and yet, once more,
He whistled, as though at a sweetheart's door.

The five men laughed at him, trapped alive;
And—the door crashed open behind the five!

Out of the stable, a wave of thunder,
Swept Black Bess, and the five went under.

He leapt to the saddle. A hoof-spurned stone
Flashed blue fire, and their prize was gone.

II

Away, through the ringing, cobbled street, and out by
the Northern Gate,
He rode that night, like a ghost in flight from the dogs
of his own fate.

By Crackskull Common, and Highgate Heath, he heard
the chase behind;
But he rode to forget—forget—forget—the hounds of his
own mind.

And cherry-black Bess on the Enfield Road flew light as
a bird to her goal;
But her Rider carried a heavier load, in his own struggling soul.

He needed neither spur nor whip. He was borne on a
darker gale.
He rode like a hurricane-hunted ship, with the doom-
wind in her sail.

He rode for the one impossible thing; that, in the morning light,
The towers of York might waken him—from London,
and last night.

He rode to prove himself another, and leave himself
behind;
And the hunted self was like a cloud; but the hunter
like the wind.

Neck and neck they rode together; that, in the day's
first gleam,
Each might prove that the other self was but a mocking
dream.

And the little sleeping villages, and the breathless
country-side,
Woke to the drum of the racing hoofs; but missed that
ghostly ride.

They did not hear, they did not see, as the drumming
hoofs drew nigh,
The dark magnificent thief in the night that rode so
subtly by.

They woke. They rushed to the wayside door. They
saw what the midnight showed,—
A mare that came like a crested wave along the Great
North Road;

A flying spark in the formless dark, a flash from the
hoof-spurned stone,
And the lifted face of a Man, that took the star-light,
and was gone.

They heard the shout of the pounding chase, three hundred yards away.
There were fourteen men in a steam of sweat and a
plaster of Midland clay.

The star-light struck their pistol-butts, as they passed in
a clattering crowd,
*But the hunting wraith was away like the wind at the
heels of the hunted cloud.*

He rode by the walls of Nottingham; and, over him as
he went,
Like ghosts across the Great North Road, the boughs of
Sherwood bent,

By Bawtry all the chase but one had dropt a league
    behind,
Yet that one Rider hunted him, invisibly, as the wind.

And northward, like a blacker night, he saw the moors
    up-loom,
And Don and Derwent sang to him, like memory in the
    gloom,

And northward, northward as he rode, and sweeter than
    a prayer
The voices of those hidden streams, the Trent and Ouse
    and Aire;

Streams that could never slake his thirst. He heard
    them as they flowed.
But one dumb Shadow hunted him along the Great
    North Road.

Till now, at dawn, the towers of York rose on the redden-
    ing sky,
And Bess went down between his knees, like a breaking
    wave, to die.

He lay beside her in the ditch. He kissed her lovely
    head;
And a Shadow passed him like the wind, and left him
    with his dead.

He saw, but not as one that wakes, the City that he
    sought;
He had escaped from London town, but not from his
    own thought.

He strode up to the Mickle-gate with none to say him
  nay;
And there he met his Other Self, in the stranger light
  of day.

He strode up to the dreadful Thing that in the gateway
  stood;
And it stretched out a ghostly hand that the dawn had
  stained with blood.

It stood, as in the gates of hell, with none to hear or see.
" Welcome! " it said, *" Thou'st ridden well; and outstript
  all but me."*

ALFRED NOYES

THE LAST BUCCANEER

Oh England is a pleasant place for them that's rich and
  high,
But England is a cruel place for such poor folks as I;
And such a port for mariners I ne'er shall see again
As the pleasant Isle of Avès, beside the Spanish Main.

There were forty craft in Avès that were both swift and
  stout,
All furnished well with small arms and cannons round
  about;
And a thousand men in Avès made laws so fair and free
To choose their valiant captains and obey them loyally.

Thence we sailed against the Spaniard with his hoards
  of plate and gold,
Which he wrung with cruel tortures from Indian folk
  of old;

91

Likewise the merchant captains, with hearts as hard as
    stone,
Who flog men and keel-haul them, and starve them to
    the bone.

Oh, the palms grew high in Avès, and fruits that shone
    like gold,
And the colibris and parrots they were gorgeous to
    behold
And the negro maids to Avès from bondage fast did flee,
To welcome gallant sailors, a-sweeping in from sea.

Oh, sweet it was in Avès to hear the landward breeze,
A-swing with good tobacco in a net between the trees,
With a negro lass to fan you, while you listened to the
    roar
Of the breakers on the reef outside, that never touched
    the shore.

But Scripture saith, an ending to all fine things must be:
So the King's ships sailed on Avès, and quite put down
    were we.
All day we fought like bulldogs, but they burst the
    booms at night;
And I fled in a piragua, sore wounded, from the fight.

Nine days I floated starving, and a negro lass beside,
Till for all I tried to cheer her, the poor young thing
    she died;
But as I lay a-gasping, a Bristol sail came by,
And brought me home to England here, to beg until I
    die.

And now I'm old and going—I'm sure I can't tell where;
One comfort is, this world's so hard, I can't be worse off
    there:
If I might but be a sea-dove, I'd fly across the main,
To the pleasant Isle of Avès, to look at it once again.

CHARLES KINGSLEY

    keel-haul] to haul a man under the keel of a ship by lowering him over the side and pulling him up on the opposite side.
    colibris] humming-birds.
    piragua] now usually written *pirogue*; an open boat.

BONNY DUNDEE
From " The Doom of Devorgoil "

To the Lords of Convention 'twas Claver'se who spoke,
" Ere the King's crown shall fall there are crowns to be
    broke;
So let each Cavalier who loves honour and me,
Come follow the bonnet of Bonny Dundee.

  "Come fill up my cup, come fill up my can,
    Come saddle your horses, and call up your men;
    Come open the West Port, and let me gang free,
    And it's room for the bonnets of Bonny Dundee! "

Dundee he is mounted, he rides up the street,
The bells are rung backward, the drums they are beat;
But the Provost, douce man, said, " Just e'en let him be,
The Gude Town is weel quit of that Deil of Dundee."

With sour-featured Whigs the Grassmarket was cramm'd
As if half the West had set tryst to be hang'd;
There was spite in each look, there was fear in each e'e,
As they watch'd for the bonnets of Bonny Dundee.

93

These cowls of Kilmarnock had spits and had spears,
And lang-hafted gullies to kill Cavaliers;
But they shrunk to close-heads, and the causeway was
    free,
At the toss of the bonnet of Bonny Dundee.

He spurr'd to the foot of the proud Castle rock,
And with the gay Gordon he gallantly spoke;
"Let Mons Meg and her marrows speak twa words or
    three,
For the love of the bonnet of Bonny Dundee."

The Gordon demands of him which way he goes—
"Where'er shall direct me the shade of Montrose!
Your Grace in short space shall hear tidings of me,
Or that low lies the bonnet of Bonny Dundee.

"There are hills beyond Pentland, and lands beyond
    Forth;
If there's lords in the Lowlands, there's chiefs in the
    North;
There are wild Duniewassals, three thousand times three,
Will cry *hoigh* for the bonnet of Bonny Dundee.

"There's brass on the target of barken'd bull-hide,
There's steel in the scabbard that dangles beside;
The brass shall be burnish'd, the steel shall flash free,
At a toss of the bonnet of Bonny Dundee.

"Away to the hills, to the caves, to the rocks—
Ere I own a usurper, I'll couch with the fox;
And tremble, false Whigs, in the midst of your glee,
You have not seen the last of my bonnet and me!"

He waved his proud hand, and the trumpets were blown.
The kettle-drums clash'd, and the horsemen rode on,
Till on Ravelston's cliffs and on Clermiston's lee,
Died away the wild war-notes of Bonny Dundee.

"Come fill up my cup, come fill up my can,
Come saddle the horses and call up the men,
Come open your gates, and let me gae free,
For it's up with the bonnets of Bonny Dundee! "

SIR WALTER SCOTT

THE CAPTAIN

(A LEGEND OF THE NAVY)

He that only rules by terror
    Doeth grievous wrong.
Deep as Hell I count his error.
    Let him hear my song.
Brave the Captain was: the seamen
    Make a gallant crew,
Gallant sons of English freemen,
    Sailors bold and true.
But they hated his oppression,
    Stern he was and rash;
So for every light transgression
    Doom'd them to the lash.
Day by day more harsh and cruel
    Seem'd the Captain's mood.
Secret wrath like smother'd fuel
    Burnt in each man's blood.
Yet he hoped to purchase glory,
    Hoped to make the name

95

Of his vessel great in story,
   Wheresoe'er he came.
So they past by capes and islands,
   Many a harbour-mouth,
Sailing under palmy highlands—
   Far within the South.
On a day when they were going
   O'er the lone expanse,
In the north, her canvas flowing,
   Rose a ship of France.
Then the Captain's colour heighten'd
   Joyful came his speech:
But a cloudy gladness lighten'd
   In the eyes of each.
"Chase," he said: the ship flew forward
   And the wind did blow;
Stately, lightly, went she Norward,
   Till she near'd the foe.
Then they look'd at him they hated,
   Had what they desired:
Mute with folded arms they waited—
   Not a gun was fired.
But they heard the foeman's thunder
   Roaring out their doom;
All the air was torn in sunder,
   Crashing went the boom,
Spars were splinter'd, decks were shatter'd,
   Bullets fell like rain;
Over mast and deck were scatter'd
   Blood and brains of men.
Spars were splinter'd; decks were broken:
   Every mother's son—

Down they dropt—no word was spoken—
  Each beside his gun.
On the decks as they were lying,
  Were their faces grim.
In their blood, as they lay dying,
  Did they smile on him.
Those, in whom he had reliance
  For his noble name,
With one smile of still defiance
  Sold him unto shame.
Shame and wrath his heart confounded,
  Pale he turn'd and red,
Till himself was deadly wounded
  Falling on the dead.
Dismal error! fearful slaughter!
  Years have wander'd by,
Side by side beneath the water
  Crew and Captain lie;
There the sunlit ocean tosses
  O'er them mouldering,
And the lonely seabird crosses
  With one waft of the wing.

LORD TENNYSON

THE RIME OF THE ANCIENT MARINER

PART I

It is an ancient Mariner,
And he stoppeth one of three.
—" By thy long grey beard and glittering
    eye,
Now wherefore stopp'st thou me?

An ancient Mariner meeteth three Gallants bidden to a wedding-feast, and detaineth one.

" The Bridegroom's doors are opened wide,
And I am next of kin;
The guests are met, the feast is set:
May'st hear the merry din."

He holds him with his skinny hand;
" There was a ship," quoth he.
—" Hold off! unhand me, grey-beard loon! "
Eftsoons his hand dropt he.

He holds him with his glittering eye—
The Wedding-Guest stood still,
And listens like a three years' child:
The Mariner hath his will.

The Wedding-Guest is spellbound by the eye of the old sea-faring man, and constrained to hear his tale.

The Wedding-Guest sat on a stone;
He cannot choose but hear;
And thus spake on that ancient man,
The bright-eyed Mariner.

" The ship was cheered, the harbour cleared,
Merrily did we drop
Below the kirk, below the hill,
Below the lighthouse top.

" The Sun came up upon the left,
Out of the sea came he!
And he shone bright, and on the right,
Went down into the sea.

The Mariner tells how the ship sailed southward with a good wind and fair weather, till it reached the Line.

" Higher and higher every day,
Till over the mast at noon "—
The Wedding-Guest here beat his breast,
For he heard the loud bassoon.

The bride hath paced into the hall,
Red as a rose is she;
Nodding their heads before her goes
The merry minstrelsy.

The Wedding-Guest heareth the bridal music; but the Mariner continueth his tale.

The Wedding-Guest he beat his breast,
Yet he cannot choose but hear;
And thus spake on that ancient man,
The bright-eyed Mariner.

" And now the storm-blast came, and he
Was tyrannous and strong:
He struck with his o'ertaking wings,
And chased us south along.

The ship driven by a storm toward the south pole.

" With sloping masts and dipping prow,
As who pursued with yell and blow
Still treads the shadow of his foe,
And forward bends his head,
The ship drove fast, loud roared the blast,
And southward aye we fled.

" And now there came both mist and snow,
And it grew wondrous cold:
And ice, mast-high, came floating by,
As green as emerald.

" And through the drifts the snowy clifts
Did send a dismal sheen:
Nor shapes of men nor beasts we ken—
The ice was all between.

The land of ice, and of fearful sounds, where no living thing was to be seen.

" The ice was here, the ice was there,
The ice was all around:

It cracked and growled, and roared and howled,
Like noises in a swound!

"At length did cross an Albatross,
Thorough the fog it came;
As if it had been a Christian soul,
We hailed it in God's name.

Till a great sea-bird, called the Albatross, came through the snow-fog, and was received with great joy and hospitality.

"It ate the food it ne'er had eat,
And round and round it flew,
The ice did split with a thunder-fit;
The helmsman steered us through!

"And a good south wind sprung up
    behind;
The Albatross did follow,
And every day, for food or play,
Came to the mariners' hollo!

And lo! the Albatross proveth a bird of good omen, and followeth the ship, as it returned northward, through fog and floating ice.

"In mist or cloud, on mast or shroud,
It perched for vespers nine;
Whiles all the night, through fog-smoke white,
Glimmered the white moonshine."

"God save thee, ancient Mariner!
From the fiends, that plague thee thus!—
Why look'st thou so?"—"With my cross-bow
I shot the Albatross.

The ancient Mariner inhospitably killeth the pious bird of good omen.

PART II

"The Sun now rose upon the right:
Out of the sea came he,
Still hid in mist—and on the left
Went down into the sea.

100

" And the good south wind still blew behind,
But no sweet bird did follow,
Nor any day, for food or play,
Came to the mariners' hollo!

" And I had done a hellish thing,
And it would work 'em woe;
For all averred, I had killed the bird
That made the breeze to blow.
' Ah wretch! ' said they, ' the bird to slay,
That made the breeze to blow! '

His shipmates cry out against the ancient Mariner, for killing the bird of good luck.

" Nor dim nor red, like God's own head,
The glorious Sun uprist:
Then all averred, I had killed the bird
That brought the fog and mist.
' 'Twas right,' said they, ' such birds to slay,
That bring the fog and mist.'

But when the fog cleared off, they justify the same, and thus make themselves accomplices in the crime.

" The fair breeze blew, the white foam
    flew,
The furrow followed free;
We were the first that ever burst
Into that silent sea.

The fair breeze continues; the ship enters the Pacific Ocean and sails northward, even till it reaches the Line.

" Down dropt the breeze, the sails dropt
    down,
'Twas sad as sad could be;
And we did speak only to break
The silence of the sea!

The ship hath been suddenly becalmed.

" All in a hot and copper sky,
The bloody Sun, at noon,
Right up above the mast did stand,
No bigger than the Moon.

" Day after day, day after day,
We stuck, nor breath nor motion;
As idle as a painted ship
Upon a painted ocean.

" Water, water, everywhere,
And all the boards did shrink;
Water, water, everywhere,
Nor any drop to drink.

And the Albatross
begins to be avenged.

" The very deep did rot: O Christ!
That ever this should be!
Yea, slimy things did crawl with legs
Upon the slimy sea.

" About, about, in reel and rout
The death-fires danced at night;
The water, like a witch's oils,
Burnt green, and blue, and white.

" And some in dreams assurèd were
Of the Spirit that plagued us so;
Nine fathom deep he had followed us
From the land of mist and snow.

A spirit had followed
them; one of the in-
visible inhabitants of
this planet, neither
departed souls nor
angels, concerning
whom the learned
Jew, Josephus, and
the Platonic Con-
stantinopolitan,
Michael Psellus, may
be consulted. They
are very numerous,
and there is no
climate or element
without one or more

" And every tongue, through utter drought,
Was withered at the root;
We could not speak, no more than if
We had been choked with soot.

" Ah! well a-day! what evil looks
Had I from old and young!
Instead of the cross, the Albatross
About my neck was hung.

The shipmates in
their sore distress
would fain throw
the whole guilt on
the ancient Mariner:
in sign whereof they
hang the dead sea-
bird round his neck.

102

Part III

" There passed a weary time. Each throat
Was parched, and glazed each eye.
A weary time! a weary time!
How glazed each weary eye!
When looking westward, I beheld
A something in the sky.

The ancient Mariner
beholdeth a sign in
the element afar off.

" At first it seemed a little speck,
And then it seemed a mist;
It moved and moved, and took at last
A certain shape, I wist.

A speck, a mist, a shape, I wist!
And still it neared and neared:
As if it dodged a water-sprite,
It plunged and tacked and veered.

" With throats unslaked, with black lips baked,
We could not laugh nor wail;
Through utter drought all dumb we stood !
I bit my arm, I sucked the blood,
And cried, ' A sail! a sail! '

At its nearer
approach, it seemeth
him to be a ship;
and at a dear ransom
he freeth his speech
from the bonds of
thirst.

" With throats unslaked, with black lips baked,
Agape they heard me call:
Gramercy! they for joy did grin,
And all at once their breath drew in,
As they were drinking all.

A flash of joy.

" ' See! see! ' (I cried) ' she tacks no more!
Hither to work us weal;
Without a breeze, without a tide,
She steadies with upright keel! '

And horror follows.
For can it be a ship
that comes onward
without wind or
tide?

" The western wave was all a-flame,
The day was well nigh done!
Almost upon the western wave
Rested the broad bright Sun;
When that strange shape drove suddenly
Betwixt us and the Sun.

" And straight the Sun was flecked with bars,
(Heaven's Mother send us grace!)
As if through a dungeon-grate he peered
With broad and burning face.

It seemeth him but the skeleton of a ship.

" Alas! (thought I, and my heart beat loud)
How fast she nears and nears!
Are those her sails that glance in the Sun,
Like restless gossameres?

" Are those her ribs through which the Sun
Did peer, as through a grate?
And is that Woman all her crew?
Is that a Death? and are there two?
Is Death that Woman's mate?

And its ribs are seen as bars on the face of the setting Sun. The spectre-woman and her death-mate, and no other on board the skeleton-ship.

" Her lips were red, her looks were free,
Her locks were yellow as gold:
Her skin was as white as leprosy,
The Nightmare Life-in-Death was she,
Who thicks man's blood with cold.

Like vessel, like crew!

" The naked hulk alongside came,
And the twain were casting dice;
' The game is done! I've won! I've won! '
Quoth she, and whistles thrice.

Death and Life-in-Death have diced for the ship's crew, and she (the latter) winneth the ancient Mariner.

" The Sun's rim dips; the stars rush out:
At one stride comes the dark;
With far-heard whisper, o'er the sea,
Off shot the spectre-bark.

No twilight within the courts of the Sun.

" We listened and looked sideways up!
Fear at my heart, as at a cup,
My life-blood seemed to sip!
The stars were dim, and thick the night,
The steersman's face by his lamp gleamed white;
From the sails the dew did drip—
Till clomb above the eastern bar
The hornèd Moon, with one bright star
Within the nether tip.

At the rising of the Moon,

" One after one, by the star-dogged Moon,
Too quick for groan or sigh,
Each turned his face with a ghastly pang,
And cursed me with his eye.

One after another,

" Four times fifty living men
(And I heard nor sigh nor groan),
With heavy thump, a lifeless lump,
They dropt down one by one.

His shipmates drop down dead.

" The souls did from their bodies fly—
They fled to bliss or woe!
And every soul, it passed me by,
Like the whizz of my cross-bow."

But Life-in-Death begins her work on the ancient Mariner.

PART IV

" I fear thee, ancient Mariner!
I fear thy skinny hand!
And thou art long, and lank, and brown,
As is the ribbed sea-sand.

The Wedding-Guest feareth that a spirit is talking to him.

" I fear thee and thy glittering eye,
And thy skinny hand so brown."—
" Fear not, fear not, thou Wedding-Guest!
This body dropt not down.

But the ancient
Mariner assureth
him of his bodily
life, and proceedeth
to relate his hor-
rible penance.

" Alone, alone, all, all alone,
Alone on a wide, wide sea!
And never a saint took pity on
My soul in agony.

" The many men, so beautiful!
And they all dead did lie:
And a thousand thousand slimy things
Lived on; and so did I.

He despiseth the
creatures of the
calm.

" I looked upon the rotting sea,
And drew my eyes away;
I looked upon the rotting deck,
And there the dead men lay.

And envieth that
they should live and
so many lie dead.

" I looked to heaven, and tried to pray;
But or ever a prayer had gusht,
A wicked whisper came, and made
My heart as dry as dust.

" I closed my lids, and kept them close,
And the balls like pulses beat;
But the sky and the sea, and the sea and the sky
Lay like a load on my weary eye,
And the dead were at my feet.

" The cold sweat melted from their limbs,
Nor rot nor reek did they:

But the curse liveth
for him in the eye
of the dead men

The look with which they looked on me
Had never passed away.

" An orphan's curse would drag to Hell
A spirit from on high;
But oh! more horrible than that
Is the curse in a dead man's eye!
Seven days, seven nights, I saw that curse,
And yet I could not die.

" The moving Moon went up the sky,
And nowhere did abide:
Softly she was going up,
And a star or two beside—

In his loneliness and fixedness he yearneth towards the journeying Moon, and the stars that still sojourn, yet still move onward; and everywhere the blue sky belongs to them, and is their appointed rest, and their native country and their own natural homes, which they enter unannounced, as lords that are certainly expected and yet there is a silent joy at their arrival.

" Her beams bemocked the sultry main
Like April hoar-frost spread;
But where the ship's huge shadow lay,
The charmèd water burnt alway
A still and awful red.

" Beyond the shadow of the ship,
I watched the water-snakes:
They moved in tracks of shining white,
And when they reared, the elfish light
Fell off in hoary flakes.

By the light of the Moon he beholdeth God's creatures of the great calm.

" Within the shadow of the ship
I watch'd their rich attire:
Blue, glossy green, and velvet black,
They coiled and swam; and every track
Was a flash of golden fire.

" O happy living things! no tongue
Their beauty might declare:

Their beauty and their happiness.

107

A spring of love gushed from my heart,
And I blessed them unaware:
Sure my kind saint took pity on me,
And I blessed them unaware.

He blesseth them in
his heart.

" The selfsame moment I could pray;
And from my neck so free
The Albatross fell off, and sank
Like lead into the sea.

The spell begins to
break.

PART V

" O sleep! it is a gentle thing,
Beloved from pole to pole!
To Mary Queen the praise be given!
She sent the gentle sleep from Heaven
That slid into my soul.

" The silly buckets on the deck
That had so long remained,
I dreamt that they were filled with dew;
And when I awoke, it rained.

By grace of the holy
Mother, the ancient
Mariner is refreshed
with rain.

" My lips were wet, my throat was cold,
My garments all were dank;
Sure I had drunken in my dreams,
And still my body drank.

" I moved, and could not feel my limbs:
I was so light—almost
I thought that I had died in sleep,
And was a blessèd ghost.

" And soon I heard a roaring wind :
It did not come anear;
But with its sound it shook the sails,
That were so thin and sere.

He heareth sounds, and seeth strange sights and commotions in the sky and the element.

" The upper air burst into life!
And a hundred fire-flags sheen,
To and fro, they were hurried about;
And to and fro, and in and out,
The wan stars danced between.

" And the coming wind did roar more loud,
And the sails did sigh like sedge;
And the rain poured down from one black cloud;
The Moon was at its edge.

" The thick black cloud was cleft, and still
The Moon was at its side :
Like waters shot from some high crag,
The lightning fell with never a jag,
A river steep and wide.

" The loud wind never reached the ship,
Yet now the ship moved on!
Beneath the lightning and the Moon
The dead men gave a groan.

The bodies of the ship's crew are inspired, and the ship moves on.

" They groaned, they stirred, they all uprose,
Nor spake, nor moved their eyes;
It had been strange, e'en in a dream,
To have seen those dead men rise.

" The helmsman steered, the ship moved on;
Yet never a breeze up blew;

The mariners all 'gan work the ropes,
Where they were wont to do;
They raised their limbs like lifeless tools—
We were a ghastly crew.

" The body of my brother's son
Stood by me, knee to knee:
The body and I pulled at one rope,
But he said nought to me."

—" I fear thee, ancient Mariner! "
—" Be calm, thou Wedding-Guest!
'Twas not those souls that fled in pain,
Which to their corses came again,
But a troop of spirits blest:

But not by the souls of the men, nor by demons of earth or middle air, but by a blessed troop of angelic spirits, sent down by the invocation of the guardian saint.

" For when it dawned—they dropped their arms,
And clustered round the mast;
Sweet sounds rose slowly through their mouths,
And from their bodies passed.

" Around, around, flew each sweet sound,
Then darted to the Sun;
Slowly the sounds came back again,
Now mixed, now one by one.

" Sometimes a-dropping from the sky
I heard the skylark sing;
Sometimes all little birds that are,
How they seemed to fill the sea and air
With their sweet jargoning!

" And now 'twas like all instruments,
Now like a lonely flute;

And now it is an angel's song,
That makes the heavens be mute.

" It ceased; yet still the sails made on
A pleasant noise till noon,
A noise like of a hidden brook
In the leafy month of June,
That to the sleeping woods all night
Singeth a quiet tune.

" Till noon we quietly sailed on,
Yet never a breeze did breathe:
Slowly and smoothly went the ship,
Moved onward from beneath.

" Under the keel nine fathom deep,
From the land of mist and snow,
The Spirit slid; and it was he
That made the ship to go.
The sails at noon left off their tune,
And the ship stood still also.

The lonesome Spirit from the South Pole carries on the ship as far as the Line, in obedience to the angelic troop, but still requireth vengeance.

" The Sun, right up above the mast,
Had fixed her to the ocean:
But in a minute she 'gan stir,
With a short uneasy motion—
Backwards and forwards half her length,
With a short uneasy motion.

" Then like a pawing horse let go,
She made a sudden bound:
It flung the blood into my head,
And I fell down in a swound.

III

" How long in that same fit I lay,
I have not to declare;
But ere my living life returned,
I heard, and in my soul discerned
Two voices in the air.

The Polar Spirit's fellow-demons, the invisible inhabitants of the element, take part in his wrong; and two of them relate, one to the other, that penance long and heavy for the ancient Mariner hath been accorded to the Polar Spirit, who returneth southward.

" ' Is it he? ' quoth one, ' is this the man?
By Him who died on cross,
With his cruel bow he laid full low
The harmless Albatross.

" ' The Spirit who bideth by himself
In the land of mist and snow,
He loved the bird that loved the man
Who shot him with his bow.'

" The other was a softer voice,
As soft as honey-dew:
Quoth he, ' The man hath penance done,
And penance more will do.'

PART VI

First Voice

" ' But tell me, tell me! speak again,
Thy soft response renewing—
What makes that ship drive on so fast?
What is the Ocean doing? '

Second Voice

" ' Still as a slave before his lord,
The Ocean hath no blast;
His great bright eye most silently
Up to the Moon is cast—

" ' If he may know which way to go;
For she guides him smooth or grim.
See, brother, see! how graciously
She looketh down on him.'

First Voice

" ' But why drives on that ship so fast,
Without or wave or wind? '

The Mariner hath been cast into a trance; for the angelic power causeth the vessel to drive northward faster than human life could endure.

Second Voice

" ' The air is cut away before,
And closes from behind.

" ' Fly, brother, fly! more high, more high!
Or we shall be belated:
For slow and slow that ship will go,
When the Mariner's trance is abated.'

" I woke, and we were sailing on
As in a gentle weather:
'Twas night, calm night, the Moon was
    high;
The dead men stood together.

The supernatural motion is retarded, the Mariner awakes, and his penance begins anew.

" All stood together on the deck,
For a charnel-dungeon fitter:
All fixed on me their stony eyes,
That in the Moon did glitter.

" The pang, the curse, with which they died,
Had never passed away:
I could not draw my eyes from theirs,
Nor turn them up to pray.

" And now this spell was snapt: once more The curse is finally expiated.
I viewed the ocean green,
And looked far forth, yet little saw
Of what had else been seen—

" Like one that on a lonesome road
Doth walk in fear and dread,
And having once turned round, walks on,
And turns no more his head;
Because he knows a frightful fiend
Doth close behind him tread.

" But soon there breathed a wind on me,
Nor sound nor motion made:
Its path was not upon the sea,
In ripple or in shade.

" It raised my hair, it fanned my cheek
Like a meadow-gale of spring—
It mingled strangely with my fears,
Yet it felt like a welcoming.

" Swiftly, swiftly flew the ship,
Yet she sailed softly too:
Sweetly, sweetly blew the breeze—
On me alone it blew.

" Oh! dream of joy! is this indeed And the ancient Mariner beholdeth his native country.
The lighthouse top I see?
Is this the hill? is this the kirk?
Is this mine own countree?

" We drifted o'er the harbour-bar,
And I with sobs did pray—

O let me be awake, my God!
Or let me sleep alway.

" The harbour-bay was clear as glass,
So smoothly it was strewn!
And on the bay the moonlight lay,
And the shadow of the Moon.

" The rock shone bright, the kirk no less,
That stands above the rock :
The moonlight steeped in silentness
The steady weathercock.

" And the bay was white with silent light,
Till, rising from the same,
Full many shapes, that shadows were,
In crimson colours came.

The angelic spirits
leave the dead
bodies.

" A little distance from the prow
Those crimson shadows were :
I turned my eyes upon the deck—
O Christ! what saw I there!

And appear in their
own forms of light.

" Each corse lay flat, lifeless and flat,
And, by the holy rood!
A man all light, a seraph-man,
On every corse there stood.

" This seraph-band, each waved his hand :
It was a heavenly sight!
They stood as signals to the land,
Each one a lovely light:

" This seraph-band, each waved his hand,
No voice did they impart—
No voice: but oh! the silence sank
Like music on my heart.

" But soon I heard the dash of oars,
I heard the Pilot's cheer;
My head was turned perforce away,
And I saw a boat appear.

" The Pilot and the Pilot's boy,
I heard them coming fast:
Dear Lord in Heaven! it was a joy
The dead men could not blast.

" I saw a third—I heard his voice:
It is the Hermit good!
He singeth loud his godly hymns
That he makes in the wood.
He'll shrieve my soul, he'll wash away
The Albatross's blood.

Part VII

" This Hermit good lives in that wood
Which slopes down to the sea.
How loudly his sweet voice he rears!
He loves to talk with marineres
That come from a far countree.

The Hermit of the Wood

" He kneels at morn, and noon, and eve—
He hath a cushion plump:
It is the moss that wholly hides
The rotted old oak-stump.

" The skiff-boat neared: I heard them talk,
' Why, this si strange, I trow!
Where are those lights so many and fair,
That signal made but now? '

" ' Strange, by my faith,' the Hermit
    said—
' And they answered not our cheer!
The planks look warped! and see those sails,
How thin they are and sere!
I never saw aught like to them,
Unless perchance it were

" ' Brown skeletons of leaves that lag
My forest-brook along;
When the ivy-tod is heavy with snow,
And the owlet whoops to the wolf below,
That eats the she-wolf's young.'

" ' Dear Lord! it hath a fiendish look '—
(The Pilot made reply)
' I am a-feared.'—' Push on, push on! '
Said the Hermit cheerily.

" The boat came closer to the ship,
But I nor spake nor stirred;
The boat came close beneath the ship,
And straight a sound was heard.

" Under the water it rumbled on,
Still louder and more dread:
It reached the ship, it split the bay;
The ship went down like lead.

Approacheth the ship with wonder.

The ship suddenly sinketh.

" Stunned by the loud and dreadful sound, The ancient Mariner is saved in the Pilot's boat.
Which sky and ocean smote,
Like one that hath been seven days drowned
My body lay afloat;
But swift as dreams, myself I found
Within the Pilot's boat.

" Upon the whirl, where sank the ship,
The boat spun round and round;
And all was still, save that the hill
Was telling of the sound.

" I moved my lips—the Pilot shrieked
And fell down in a fit;
The holy Hermit raised his eyes,
And prayed where he did sit.

" I took the oars: the Pilot's boy,
Who now doth crazy go,
Laughed loud and long, and all the while
His eyes went to and fro.
' Ha! ha! ' quoth he, ' full plain I see
The Devil knows how to row.'

" And now, all in my own countree,
I stood on the firm land.
The Hermit stepped forth from the boat,
And scarcely he could stand.

" ' O shrieve me, shrieve me, holy man! ' The ancient Mariner earnestly entreateth the Hermit to shrieve him: and the penance of life falls on him.
The Hermit crossed his brow,
' Say quick,' quoth he, ' I bid thee say—
What manner of man art thou? '

118

" Forthwith this frame of mine was wrenched
With a woful agony,
Which forced me to begin my tale;
And then it left me free.

" Since then, at an uncertain hour,
That agony returns:
And till my ghastly tale is told,
This heart within me burns.

And ever and anon
throughout his future
life an agony con-
straineth him to
travel from land to
land:

" I pass, like night, from land to land;
I have strange power of speech;
That moment that his face I see,
I know the man that must hear me:
To him my tale I teach.

" What loud uproar bursts from that door!
The wedding-guests are there:
But in the garden-bower the bride
And bridemaids singing are:
And hark, the little vesper bell,
Which biddeth me to prayer!

" O Wedding-Guest! this soul hath been
Alone on a wide, wide sea;
So lonely 'twas, that God Himself
Scarce seemèd there to be.

" O sweeter than the marriage-feast,
'Tis sweeter far to me,
To walk together to the kirk
With a goodly company!—

" To walk together to the kirk,
And all together pray,
While each to his great Father bends,
Old men, and babes, and loving friends,
And youths and maidens gay!

" Farewell, farewell! but this I tell
To thee, thou Wedding-Guest!
He prayeth well, who loveth well
Both man and bird and beast.

And to teach by his own example, love and reverence to all things that God made and loveth.

" He prayeth best, who loveth best
All things both great and small;
For the dear God who loveth us,
He made and loveth all."

The Mariner, whose eye is bright,
Whose beard with age is hoar,
Is gone: and now the Wedding-Guest
Turned from the bridegroom's door.

He went like one that hath been stunned,
And is of sense forlorn:
A sadder and a wiser man,
He rose the morrow morn.

SAMUEL TAYLOR COLERIDGE

THE LIGHTHOUSE

Just as my watch was done, the fog had lifted,
And we could see the flashing of our light,
And see once more the reef beyond the Head

Over which six days and nights the mist had drifted,
Until it seemed all time to mist had drifted
And day and night were but one blind white night.

But on the seventh midnight the wind shifted,
And I was glad to tumble into bed,
Thankful to hear no more the blaring horn
That ceaselessly had sounded, night and morn
With moaning echoes through the mist to warn
The blind bewildered ships at sea:
Yet, though as tired as any dog,
I lay awhile and seemed to feel
Fog lying on my eyes still heavily,
And still the horn unceasingly
Sang through my head, till gradually
Through night's strange stillness over me
Sweet sleep began to steal,
Sleep blind and thick and fleecy as the fog.
For all I knew, I might have slept
A moment—or eternity,
When, startled by a crash,
I waked to find I'd leapt
Upright on the floor;
And stood there listening to the smash
Of falling glass . . . and then a thud
Of something heavy tumbling
Into the next room . . .
A pad of naked feet . . .
A moan . . . a sound of stumbling . . .
A heavier thud . . . and then no more.
And I stood shivering in the gloom,
With creeping flesh and tingling blood,

Until I gave myself a shake
To bring my wits more wide awake,
And lit a lanthorn and flung wide the door.
Half-dazed and dazzled by the light,
At first it seemed I'd only find
A broken pane, a flapping blind;
But when I raised the lanthorn o'er my head
I saw a naked boy upon the bed
Who crouched and shuddered on the folded sheet,
And on his face before my feet
A naked man who lay as if quite dead,
Though on his broken knuckles blood was red;
And all my wits awakened at the sight.
I set the lanthorn down and took the child,
Who looked at me, with piteous eyes and wild,
And chafed his chill wet body till it glowed,
And forcing spirit 'twixt his chattering teeth,
I tucked him snugly in beneath
The blankets and soon left him warmly stowed;
And stooped to tend the man who lay
Still senseless on the floor.
I turned him off his face
And laid him on the other bed,
And washed and staunched his wound;
And yet, for all that I could do,
I could not bring him to,
Or see a trace
Of life returning to that heavy head.

It seemed he'd swooned
When through the window he'd made way,
Just having strength to lay

The boy in safety. Still as death
He lay without a breath;
And, seeing I could do no more
To help him in the fight for life,
I turned again to tend the lad,
And as I looked on him was glad
To find him sleeping quietly.
So, fetching fuel, I lit a fire
And quickly had as big a blaze
As any housewife could desire:
Then 'twixt the beds I set a chair,
That I might watch until they stirred:
And as I saw them lying there—
The sleeping boy and him who lay
In that strange stiller sleep, 'twas plain
That they were son and father, now
I'd time to look and wonder how
In such a desperate plight,
Without a stitch or rag,
They'd taken refuge from the night.
And, as I wondered drowsily,
It seemed yet queerer and more queer
For round the Head the rocks are sheer,
With scarce a foothold for a bird,
And it seemed quite beyond belief
That any wrecked upon that reef
Could swim ashore and scale the crag
By daylight, let alone by night.

But they who live beside the sea
Know naught's too wonderful to be:]
And as I sat and heard

The quiet breathing of the child
Great weariness came over me,
And in a kind of daze
I watched the blaze
With nodding head,
And must have slept, for presently
I found the man was sitting up in bed,
And talking to himself with wide unseeing eyes.
At first, I hardly made out what he said:
But soon his voice, so hoarse and wild,
Grew calm, and, straining, I could hear
The broken words that came with many sighs.

" Yes, lad: she's going: but there's naught to fear,
For I can swim and tow you in the belt.
Come, let's join hands together and leap clear. . . .
Ay, son, it's dark and cold . . . but you have felt
The cold and dark before . . .
And you should scorn . . .
And we must be near shore . . .
For hark, the horn!
Think of your mother and your home and leap. . . .
You would not leave her lonely?
She thinks of us, lad, waking or asleep. . . .
Nay! . . . then . . . go! . . .
Well done, lad! . . . Nay! I'm here. . . .
Ay, son, it's cold: but you're too big to fear.
Now then you're snug: I've got you safe in tow:
The worst is over and we've only
To make for land . . . we've naught . . . to do . . .
but steer . . .
But steer . . . but steer. . . ."

He paused and sank down in the bed, quite done,
And lay a moment silent, while his son
Still slumbered in the other bed,
And on his quiet face the firelight shone:
Then once again the father raised his head
And rambled on. . . .
" Say, lad, what cheer?
I thought you'd dropped asleep, but you're all
*   right.*
We'll rest a moment. . . . I'm quite out of breath. . . .
It's further than . . . Nay, son! there's naught to
*   fear . . .*
The land must be quite near. . . .
The horn is loud enough!
Only your father's out of puff:
He's getting fat and lazy, is your dad.
Ay, lad,
It's cold;
But you're too old
To cry for cold.
Now . . . keep . . . tight hold,
And we'll be off again.
I've got my breath. . . ."

He sank once more as still as death,
With hands that clutched the counterpane:
But still the boy was sleeping quietly.
And then, the father sat up suddenly
And cried *See! See!*
The land! the land!
It's near . . . I touch it with my hand.
And now *Oh God!* he moaned.

Small wonder, when he saw what lay before—
The black unbroken crags so grim and high
That must have seemed to him to soar
Sheer from the sea's edge to the sky.
But soon he plucked up heart, once more:
" *We're safe, lad—safe ashore!*
A narrow ledge, but land, firm land.
We'll soon be high and dry.
Nay, son, we can't stay here:
The waves would have us back
Or we should perish of the cold.
Come, lad, there's naught to fear. . . .
You must be brave and bold.
Perhaps we'll strike a track.
Ay, son, it's steep, and black
And slimy to the hold;
But we must climb, and see! the mist is gone:
The stars are shining clear. . . .
Think, son, your mother's at the top,
And you'll be up in no time. See, that star,
The brightest star that ever shone,
Just think it's she who watches you
And knows that you'll be brave and true.
Come, lad, we may not stop . . .
Or, else, the cold . . .
Give me your hand . . .
Your foot there now . . . just room to stand.
It cannot be so far. . . .
We'll soon be up . . . this work should make us warm.
Thank God it's not a storm,
Or we should scarce . . . your foot here firm. . . .
Nay, lad! you must not squirm.

126

Come, be a man: you shall not fall:
I'll hold you tight.
There now you are my own son after all!
Your mother, lad,
Her star burns bright . . .
And we're already half-way up the height. . . .
Your mother will be glad,
Ay, she'll be glad to hear
Of her brave boy who had no fear. . . .
Your foot . . . your hand . . . 'twas but a bird
You startled out of bed:
'Twould think it queer
To wake up suddenly and see your head;
And when you stirred . . .
Nay! steady, lad!
Or you will send your dad . . .
Your hand . . . your foot . . . we'll rest upon the
     ledge. . . .
Why, son, we're at the top! I feel the edge
And grass—soft dewy grass!
Let go one moment and I'll draw you up. . . .
Now, lad! . . . Thank God that's past! . . .
And you are safe, at last:
You're safe, you're safe . . . and now my precious lass
Will see her son, her little son, again.

I never thought to reach the top to-night.
God! What a height!
Nay, but you must not look: 'twould turn your head:
And we must not stand shivering here. . . .
And see! . . . a flashing light. . . .
It's sweeping towards us, and now you stand bright.

Ah, your poor, bleeding hands and feet!
My little son, my sweet!
There's nothing more to fear.
A lighthouse, lad!   And we must make for it.
You're tired; I'll carry you a bit.
Nay, son: 'twill warm me up . . .
And there will be a fire and bed,
And even perhaps a cup
Of something hot to drink,
And something good to eat.
And think, son, only think—
Your home . . . and mother . . . once again!

Once more the weary head
Sank back upon the bed;
And for a while he hardly stirred,
But only muttered now and then
A broken word,
As though to cheer
His son who still slept quietly
Upon the other side of me.

And then, my blood ran cold to hear
A sudden cry of fear:
"*My son!   My son!*
Ah God, he's done!
I thought I'd laid him on the bed. . . .
I've laid him on white mist instead:
He's fallen sheer. . . ."

Then I sprang up and cried: *Your son is here!*
And taking up the sleeping boy
I bore him to his father's arms,

And as he nestled to his breast,
Kind life came back to those wild eyes
And filled them with deep joy,
And free of all alarms
The son and father lay
Together in sweet rest,
While through the window stole the strange clear light
    of day.

WILFRID W. GIBSON

THE RIDER AT THE GATE

A windy night was blowing on Rome,
The cressets guttered on Caesar's home,
The fish-boats, moored at the bridge, were breaking
The rush of the river to yellow foam.

The hinges whined to the shutters shaking,
When clip-clop-clep came a horse-hoof raking
The stones of the road at Caesar's gate;
The spear-butts jarred at the guard's awaking.

"Who goes there?" said the guard at the gate.
"What is the news, that you ride so late?"
"News most pressing, that must be spoken
To Caesar alone, and that cannot wait."

"The Caesar sleeps: you must show a token
That the news suffice that he be awoken.
What is the news, and whence do you come?
For no light cause may his sleep be broken."

"Out of the dark of the sands I come,
From the dark of death, with news for Rome.
A word so fell that it must be uttered
Though it strike the soul of the Caesar dumb."

Caesar turned in his bed and muttered,
With a struggle for breath the lamp-flame guttered;
Calpurnia heard her husband moan:
  "The house is falling,
The beaten men come into their own."

"Speak your word," said the guard at the gate;
"Yes, but bear it to Caesar straight,
Say, 'Your murderer's knives are honing,
Your killer's gang is lying in wait.'

"Out of the wind that is blowing and moaning,
Through the city palace and the country loaning,
I cry, 'For the world's sake, Caesar, beware,
And take this warning as my atoning.

"'Beware of the Court, of the palace stair,
Of the downcast friend who speaks so fair,
Keep from the Senate, for Death is going
On many men's feet to meet you there.'

"I, who am dead, have ways of knowing
Of the crop of death that the quick are sowing.
I, who was Pompey, cry it aloud
From the dark of death, from the wind blowing.

"I, who was Pompey, once was proud,
Now I lie in the sand without a shroud;
I cry to Caesar out of my pain,
'Caesar, beware, your death is vowed.'"

loaning] field, common.

130

The light grew grey on the window-pane,
The windcocks swung in a burst of rain,
The window of Caesar flung unshuttered,
The horse-hoofs died into wind again.

Caesar turned in his bed and muttered,
With a struggle for breath the lamp-flame guttered;
Calpurnia heard her husband moan:
   "The house is falling,
The beaten men come into their own."

JOHN MASEFIELD

THE RAVEN

Once upon a midnight dreary, while I pondered, weak
      and weary,
Over many a quaint and curious volume of forgotten
      lore,
   While I nodded, nearly napping, suddenly there came
      a tapping,
   As of someone gently rapping, rapping at my chamber
      door.
" 'Tis some visitor," I muttered, " tapping at my cham-
      ber door—
      Only this, and nothing more."

   Ah, distinctly I remember it was in the bleak Decem-
      ber,
And each separate dying ember wrought its ghost upon
      the floor.
   Eagerly I wished the morrow;—vainly I had sought to
      borrow

From my books surcease of sorrow—sorrow for the
   lost Lenore—
For the rare and radiant maiden whom the angels named
   Lenore—
   Nameless here for evermore.

And the silken sad uncertain rustling of each purple
   curtain
Thrilled me—filled me with fantastic terrors never felt
   before;
So that now, to still the beating of my heart, I stood
   repeating,
" 'Tis some visitor entreating entrance at my chamber
   door—
Some late visitor entreating entrance at my chamber
   door;—
   This it is, and nothing more."

Presently my soul grew stronger; hesitating then no
   longer,
" Sir," said I, " or Madam, truly your forgiveness I implore;
But the fact is I was napping, and so gently you came
   rapping,
And so faintly you came tapping, tapping at my
   chamber door,
That I scarce was sure I heard you "—here I opened wide
   the door;—
   Darkness there, and nothing more.

Deep into that darkness peering, long I stood there
   wondering, fearing,

Doubting, dreaming dreams no mortals ever dared to
   dream before;
   But the silence was unbroken, and the darkness gave
      no token,
   And the only word there spoken was the whispered
      word, "Lenore!"
This I whispered, and an echo murmured back the word,
   "Lenore!"
      Merely this, and nothing more.

Back into the chamber turning, all my soul within me
   burning,
Soon again I heard a tapping somewhat louder than
   before.
   "Surely," said I, "surely that is something at my
      window lattice:
   Let me see, then, what thereat is, and this mystery
      explore—
Let my heart be still a moment and this mystery
   explore;—
      'Tis the wind, and nothing more."

Open here I flung the shutter, when, with many a flirt
   and flutter,
In there stepped a stately raven of the saintly days of
   yore;
   Not the least obeisance made he; not an instant
      stopped or stayed he;
   But, with mien of lord or lady, perched above my
      chamber door—
Perched upon a bust of Pallas just above my chamber
   door—
      Perched, and sat, and nothing more.

Then this ebony bird beguiling my sad fancy into
 smiling,
By the grave and stern decorum of the countenance it
 wore,
 "Though thy crest be shorn and shaven, thou," I said,
  " art sure no craven,
 Ghastly grim and ancient Raven wandering from the
  Nightly shore—
Tell me what thy lordly name is on the Night's Plu-
 tonian shore! "
    Quoth the raven, " Nevermore."

Much I marvelled this ungainly fowl to hear discourse
 so plainly,
Though its answer little meaning—little relevancy
 bore;
 For we cannot help agreeing that no living human
  being
 Ever yet was blessed with seeing bird above his chamber door—
Bird or beast upon the sculptured bust above his chamber door,
    With such name as " Nevermore."

But the raven, sitting lonely on the placid bust, spoke
 only
That one word, as if his soul in that one word he did
 outpour.
 Nothing further then he uttered—not a feather then
  he fluttered—
 Till I scarcely more than muttered, "Other friends
  have flown before—

On the morrow *he* will leave me, as my hopes have flown
  before."
  Then the bird said, " Nevermore."

Startled at the stillness broken by reply so aptly
  spoken,
" Doubtless," said I, " what it utters is its only stock and
  store,
  Caught from some unhappy master whom unmerciful
    Disaster
  Followed fast and followed faster till his songs one
    burden bore—
Till the dirges of his Hope that melancholy burden bore
  Of ' Never—nevermore.' "

But the raven still beguiling all my fancy into smil-
  ing,
Straight I wheeled a cushioned seat in front of bird, and
  bust and door;
  Then upon the velvet sinking, I betook myself to
    linking
  Fancy unto fancy, thinking what this ominous bird of
    yore—
What this grim, ungainly, ghastly, gaunt and ominous
  bird of yore
  Meant in croaking " Nevermore."

This I sat engaged in guessing, but no syllable express-
  ing
To the fowl whose fiery eyes now burned into my bosom's
  core;
  This and more I sat divining, with my head at ease
    reclining

135

On the cushion's velvet lining that the lamplight
gloated o'er,
But whose velvet violet lining with the lamplight gloat-
ing o'er,
    She shall press, ah, nevermore!

Then methought the air grew denser, perfumed from
an unseen censer
Swung by angels whose faint footsteps tinkled on the
tufted floor.
    "Wretch," I cried, " thy God hath lent thee—by these
angels He hath sent thee
Respite—respite and nepenthe, from thy memories of
Lenore!
Quaff, oh, quaff this kind nepenthe and forget this lost
Lenore! "
    Quoth the raven, " Nevermore."

"Prophet! " said I, " thing of evil!—prophet still, if
bird or devil!—
Whether Tempter sent, or whether tempest tossed thee
here ashore,
    Desolate yet all undaunted, on this desert land en-
chanted—
    On this home by Horror haunted—tell me truly, I
implore—
Is there—*is* there balm in Gilead?—tell me—tell me, I
implore! "
    Quoth the raven, " Nevermore."

"Prophet! " said I, " thing of evil—prophet still, if
bird or devil!

By that Heaven that bends above us—by that God we
    both adore—
  Tell this soul with sorrow laden if, within the distant
    Aidenn,
  It shall clasp a sainted maiden whom the angels name
    Lenore—
Clasp a rare and radiant maiden whom the angels name
    Lenore."
        Quoth the raven, " Nevermore."

" Be that word our sign of parting, bird or fiend! " I
    shrieked, upstarting—
" Get thee back into the tempest and the Night's Plu-
    tonian shore!
  Leave no black plume as a token of that lie thy soul
    hath spoken!
  Leave my loneliness unbroken!—quit the bust above
    my door!
Take thy beak from out my heart, and take thy form
    from off my door! "
        Quoth the raven, " Nevermore."

And the Raven, never flitting, still is sitting, still is
    sitting
On the pallid bust of Pallas just above my chamber door;
  And his eyes have all the seeming of a demon's that is
    dreaming,
  And the lamplight o'er him streaming throws his
    shadow on the floor;
And my soul from out that shadow that lies floating on
    the floor
        Shall be lifted—nevermore!

                       EDGAR ALLAN POE

                  E*

THE *REVENGE*

(A BALLAD OF THE FLEET)

At Florés in the Azores Sir Richard Grenville lay,
And a pinnace, like a fluttered bird, came flying from
far away:
"Spanish ships of war at sea! we have sighted fifty-
three!"
Then sware Lord Thomas Howard: "'Fore God I am no
coward;
But I cannot meet them here, for my ships are out of
gear,
And the half my men are sick. I must fly, but follow
quick.
We are six ships of the line; can we fight with fifty-
three?"

Then spake Sir Richard Grenville: "I know you are no
coward;
You fly them for a moment to fight with them again.
But I've ninety men and more that are lying sick ashore.
I should count myself the coward if I left them, my Lord
Howard,
To these Inquisition dogs and the devildoms of Spain."

So Lord Howard passed away with five ships of war that
day,
Till he melted like a cloud in the silent summer heaven;
But Sir Richard bore in hand all his sick men from the
land
Very carefully and slow,

138

Men of Bideford in Devon,
And we laid them on the ballast down below;
For we brought them all aboard,
And they blest him in their pain, that they were not left
  to Spain,
To the thumbscrew and the stake, for the glory of the
  Lord.

He had only a hundred seamen to work the ship and to
  fight,
And he sailed away from Florés till the Spaniard came
  in sight,
With his huge sea-castles heaving upon the weather bow.
" Shall we fight or shall we fly?
Good Sir Richard, tell us now,
For to fight is but to die!
There'll be little of us left by the time this sun be set."
And Sir Richard said again: " We be all good English
  men.
Let us bang those dogs of Seville, the children of the
  devil,
For I never turned my back upon Don or devil yet."

Sir Richard spoke and he laughed, and we roared a
  hurrah, and so
The little *Revenge* ran on sheer into the heart of the foe,
With her hundred fighters on deck, and her ninety sick
  below;
For half their fleet to the right and half to the left were
  seen
And the little *Revenge* ran on through the long sea-lane
  between.

Thousands of their soldiers looked down from their
    decks and laughed.
Thousands of their seamen made mock at the mad little
    craft
Running on and on, till delayed
By their mountain-like *San Philip* that, of fifteen hun-
    dred tons,
And up-shadowing high above us with her yawning tiers
    of guns,
Took the breath from our sails, and we stayed.

And while now the great *San Philip* hung above us like
    a cloud
Whence the thunderbolt will fall
Long and loud,
Four galleons drew away
From the Spanish fleet that day,
And two upon the larboard and two upon the starboard
    lay,
And the battle thunder broke from them all.

But anon the great *San Philip*, she bethought herself and
    went.
Having that within her womb that had left her ill
    content;
And the rest they came aboard us, and they fought us
    hand to hand.
For a dozen times they came with their pikes and mus-
    queteers,
And a dozen times we shook 'em off as a dog that shakes
    his ears
When he leaps from the water to the land.

And the sun went down, and the stars came out far over
the summer sea,
But never a moment ceased the fight of the one and the
fifty-three.
Ship after ship, the whole night long, their high-built
galleons came,
Ship after ship, the whole night long, with her battle-
thunder and flame;
Ship after ship, the whole night long, drew back with
her dead and her shame.
For some were sunk and many were shattered, and so
could fight us no more—
God of battles, was ever a battle like this in the world
before?

For he said, "Fight on! fight on!"
Though his vessel was all but a wreck;
And it chanced that, when half of the short summer
night was gone,
With a grisly wound to be drest he had left the deck,
But a bullet struck him that was dressing it suddenly
dead,
And himself he was wounded again in the side and the
head,
And he said, "Fight on! fight on!"

And the night went down and the sun smiled out far
over the summer sea,
And the Spanish fleet with broken sides lay round us all
in a ring;
But they dared not touch us again, for they feared that
we still could sting,
So they watched what the end would be.

And we had not fought them in vain,
But in perilous plight were we,
Seeing forty of our poor hundred were slain,
And half the rest of us maimed for life
In the crash of the cannonades and the desperate
    strife;
And the sick men down in the hold were most of them
    stark and cold,
And the pikes were all broken or bent, and the powder
    was all of it spent;
And the masts and the rigging were lying over the side;
But Sir Richard cried in his English pride,
"We have fought such a fight for a day and a night,
As may never be fought again!
We have won great glory, my men!
And a day less or more
At sea or ashore,
We die—does it matter when?
Sink me the ship, Master Gunner—sink her, split her in
    twain!
Fall into the hands of God, not into the hands of Spain!"

And the gunner said, "Ay, ay," but the seamen made
    reply:
"We have children, we have wives,
And the Lord hath spared our lives.
We will make the Spaniard promise, if we yield, to let
    us go;
We shall live to fight again and to strike another
    blow."
And the lion there lay dying, and they yielded to the
    foe.

And the stately Spanish men to their flagship bore him
    then,
Where they laid him by the mast, old Sir Richard caught
    at last,
And they praised him to his face with their courtly
    foreign grace;
But he rose upon their decks, and he cried:
"I have fought for Queen and Faith like a valiant man
    and true;
I have only done my duty as a man is bound to do;
With a joyful spirit I Sir Richard Grenville die!"
And he fell upon their decks, and he died.

And they stared at the dead that had been so valiant and
    true,
And had holden the power and glory of Spain so
    cheap
That he dared her with one little ship and his English
    few;
Was he devil or man? He was devil for aught they
    knew,
But they sank his body with honour down into the deep,
And they manned the *Revenge* with a swarthier alien
    crew,
And away she sailed with her loss and longed for her
    own;
When a wind from the lands they had ruined awoke
    from sleep,
And the water began to heave and the weather to moan,
And or ever that evening a great gale blew,
And a wave like the wave that is raised by an earthquake
    grew,

Till it smote on their hulls and their sails and their
    masts and their flags,
And the whole sea plunged and fell on the shot-shattered
    navy of Spain,
And the little *Revenge* herself went down by the island
    crags
To be lost evermore in the main.

LORD TENNYSON

OLD SIR WALTER

(A STORY OF 1734)

Stout Sir Walter was old but hearty:
    A velvet cap on his long grey hair,
A full white rose at his gold-laced button:
    Many were laughing, but none looked gayer.

Such a beast was his jet black hunter,
    Silver-spotted with foam and froth,
Brawny in flank and fiery-blooded,
    Stung by the spur to a curbless wrath!

Gaily blowing his horn, he scrambled
    Over the stone wall four feet two;
See saw over the old park railing,
    Shaking the thistle-head rich with dew.

A long black face the sour Whig huntsman
    Pulled, when he saw Sir Walter come
Trotting up gay by the oak wood cover.
    Why when he cheered did they all sit dumb?

Why when he flung up his hat and shouted,
  "God save King George! " they bawling cried,
As a Justice, drawing a long-sealed parchment,
  Rode up grim to Sir Walter's side.

"In King George's name, arrest him, lieges!
  This is the villain who fought at Boyne:
He sliced the feather from off my beaver,
  And ran his sword twice into my groin."

Then out whipp'd blades: the horns they sounded.
  The field came flocking in thick and fast,
But Sir Walter flogged at the barking rabble,
  And through them all like a whirlwind pass'd.

"A hundred guineas to seize the traitor! "
  Cried the Justice, purple and white with rage,
Then such a spurring, whipping, and flogging,
  Was never seen in the strangest age.

The hunter whipped off Spot and Fowler,
  Viper and Fury, and all the pack,
And set them fast, with their red tongues lolling
  And white teeth fix'd, on Sir Walter's track.

Loud on the wind came blast of bugle,
  All together the hounds gave tongue,
They swept like a hail-storm down by the gibbet,
  Where the black rags still in the cold storm hung.

The rain cut faces like long whip lashes,
  The wind blew strong in its wayward will,
And powdering fast, the men and horses,
  Thundering swept down Frampton Hill.

There half the grooms at last pull'd bridle.
　Swearing 'twould ruin their bits of blood;
Three Whig rogues flew out of the saddle,
　And two were plumped in the river mud.

Three men stuck to the leading rebel;
　The first was a Whig lord, fat and red,
The next a yellow-faced lean attorney,
　And the last a Justice, as some one said.

Slap at the fence went old Sir Walter,
　Slap at the ditch by the pollard-tree,
Crash through the hazels, over the water,
　And wherever he went, there went the three.

Into the hill-fence broke Sir Walter,
　Right through the tangle of branch and thorns,
Swish'd the rasper up by the windmill,
　In spite of the cries and blowing of horns.

Lines of flames trailed all the scarlet
　Streaming, the dogs half a mile before,
Whoop! with a cry all after Sir Walter,
　Driving wildly along the shore.

Over the timber flew old Sir Walter,
　Light as a swallow, sure and swift,
For his sturdy arm and his " pull and hustle "
　Could help a nag at the deadest lift.

Off went his gold-laced hat and bugle,
　His scarlet cloak he then let fall,
And into the river spurr'd old Sir Walter,
　Boldly there, in the sight of all.

There was many a sore on back and wither,
    Many a spur that ran with red,
But none of them caught the stout Sir Walter,
    Though they counted of horses sixty head.

There was many a fetlock cut and wounded,
    Many a hock deep lam'd with thorns,
Many a man that two years after
    Shuddered to hear the sound of horns.

But on the fallow, the long clay fallow,
    Foundered his black mare, Lilly Lee,
And Sir Walter sat on the tough old saddle,
    Waiting the coming of all the three.

Never such chase of stag or vermin,
    Along the park pale, in and out;
On they thundered, fast over the railing,
    Driving the fence in splints about.

The first he shot with his long steel pistol,
    The second he slew with his Irish sword,
The third he threw in the brook, and mounted
    Quick on the steed of the fat Whig lord.

Then off to the ship at the nearest harbour
    Gallop'd Sir Walter, sure and fleet.
He died, 'tis true, in an old French garret,
    But his heart went true to the latest beat.

.   .   .   .   .   •

A white rose, stifled and very sickly,
    Pined for air at the window-sill,
But the last fond look of the brave old trooper
    Was fixed on the dying emblem—still.

All alone in the dusky garret,
   He turn'd to the flower with a father's pride,
"God save King James!" the old man murmured,
  "God—save—the—King!" he moaned and died.

GEORGE WALTER THORNBURY

THE BURIAL OF SIR JOHN MOORE

AFTER CORUNNA

Not a drum was heard, not a funeral note,
   As his corse to the rampart we hurried;
Not a soldier discharged his farewell shot
   O'er the grave where our hero we buried.

We buried him darkly at dead of night,
   The sods with our bayonets turning,
By the struggling moonbeam's misty light
   And the lanthorn dimly burning.

No useless coffin enclosed his breast,
   Not in sheet or in shroud we wound him;
But he lay like a warrior taking his rest
   With his martial cloak around him.

Few and short were the prayers we said,
   And we spoke not a word of sorrow;
But we steadfastly gazed on the face that was dead,
   And we bitterly thought of the morrow.

We thought, as we hollow'd his narrow bed
　And smooth'd down his lonely pillow,
That the foe and the stranger would tread o'er his head,
　And we far away on the billow!

Lightly they'll talk of the spirit that's gone,
　And o'er his cold ashes upbraid him—
But little he'll reck, if they let him sleep on
　In the grave where a Briton has laid him.

But half of our heavy task was done
　When the clock struck the hour for retiring;
And we heard the distant and random gun
　That the foe was sullenly firing.

Slowly and sadly we laid him down,
　From the field of his fame fresh and gory;
We carved not a line, and we raised not a stone,
　But we left him alone with his glory.

CHARLES WOLFE

THE LADY OF SHALOTT

Part I

On either side the river lie
Long fields of barley and of rye,
That clothe the wold and meet the sky;
And thro' the field the road runs by
　　To many-tower'd Camelot;
And up and down the people go,
Gazing where the lilies blow
Round an island there below,
　　The island of Shalott.

Willows whiten, aspens quiver,
Little breezes dusk and shiver
Thro' the wave that runs for ever
By the island in the river
  Flowing down to Camelot.
Four grey walls, and four grey towers,
Overlook a space of flowers,
And the silent isle imbowers
  The Lady of Shalott.

By the margin, willow-veil'd,
Slide the heavy barges trail'd
By slow horses; and unhail'd
The shallop flitteth silken-sail'd
  Skimming down to Camelot:
But who hath seen her wave her hand?
Or at the casement seen her stand?
Or is she known in all the land,
  The Lady of Shalott?

Only reapers, reaping early
In among the bearded barley,
Hear a song that echoes cheerly
From the river winding clearly,
  Down to tower'd Camelot:
And by the moon the reaper weary,
Piling sheaves in uplands airy,
Listening, whispers, " 'Tis the fairy
  Lady of Shalott."

PART II

There she weaves by night and day
A magic web with colours gay,

She has heard a whisper say,
A curse is on her if she stay
    To look down to Camelot.
She knows not what the curse may be,
And so she weaveth steadily,
And little other care hath she,
    The Lady of Shalott.

And moving thro' a mirror clear
That hangs before her all the year,
Shadows of the world appear.
There she sees the highway near
    Winding down to Camelot:
There the river eddy whirls,
And there the surly village-churls,
And the red cloaks of market girls,
    Pass onward from Shalott.

Sometimes a troop of damsels glad,
An abbot on an ambling pad,
Sometimes a curly shepherd-lad,
Or long-hair'd page in crimson clad,
    Goes by to tower'd Camelot;
And sometimes thro' the mirror blue
The knights come riding two and two:
She hath no loyal knight and true,
    The Lady of Shalott.

But in her web she still delights
To weave the mirror's magic sights,
For often thro' the silent nights
A funeral, with plumes and lights,
    And music, went to Camelot:

Or when the moon was overhead,
Came two young lovers lately wed;
" I am half sick of shadows," said
    The Lady of Shalott.

Part III

A bow-shot from her bower-eaves,
He rode between the barley-sheaves,
The sun came dazzling thro' the leaves,
And flamed upon the brazen greaves
    Of bold Sir Lancelot.
A red-cross knight for ever kneel'd
To a lady in his shield,
That sparkled on the yellow field,
    Beside remote Shalott.

The gemmy bridle glitter'd free,
Like to some branch of stars we see
Hung in the golden Galaxy.
The bridle bells rang merrily
    As he rode down to Camelot:
And from his blazon'd baldric slung
A mighty silver bugle hung,
And as he rode his armour rung,
    Beside remote Shalott.

All in the blue unclouded weather
Thick-jewell'd shone the saddle leather,
The helmet and the helmet-feather
Burn'd like one burning flame together,
    As he rode down to Camelot.

As often thro' the purple night,
Below the starry clusters bright,
Some bearded meteor, trailing light,
  Moves over still Shalott.

His broad clear brow in sunlight glow'd;
On burnish'd hooves his war-horse trode;
From underneath his helmet flow'd
His coal-black curls as on he rode,
  As he rode down to Camelot.
From the bank and from the river
He flash'd into the crystal mirror,
"Tirra lirra," by the river
  Sang Sir Lancelot.

She left the web, she left the loom,
She made three paces thro' the room,
She saw the water-lily bloom,
She saw the helmet and the plume,
  She look'd down to Camelot.
Out flew the web and floated wide;
The mirror crack'd from side to side;
"The curse is come upon me," cried
  The Lady of Shalott.

PART IV

In the stormy east-wind straining,
The pale yellow woods were waning,
The broad stream in his banks complaining,
Heavily the low sky raining
  Over tower'd Camelot;

Down she came and found a boat
Beneath a willow left afloat,
And round about the prow she wrote
    The Lady of Shalott.

And down the river's dim expanse—
Like some bold seër in a trance,
Seeking all his own mischance—
With a glassy countenance
    Did she look to Camelot.
And at the closing of the day
She loosed the chain, and down she lay;
The broad stream bore her far away,
    The Lady of Shalott.

Lying, robed in snowy white
That loosely flew to left and right—
The leaves upon her falling light—
Thro' the noises of the night
    She floated down to Camelot:
And as the boat-head wound along
The willowy hills and fields among,
They heard her singing her last song,
    The Lady of Shalott.

Heard a carol, mournful, holy,
Chanted loudly, chanted lowly,
Till her blood was frozen slowly,
And her eyes were darken'd wholly,
    Turn'd to tower'd Camelot;
For ere she reach'd upon the tide
The first house by the water-side,
Singing in her song she died,
    The Lady of Shalott.

Under tower and balcony,
By garden-wall and gallery,
A gleaming shape she floated by,
Dead-pale between the houses high,
    Silent into Camelot.
Out upon the wharfs they came,
Knight and burgher, lord and dame,
And round the prow they read her name,
    The Lady of Shalott.

Who is this? and what is here?
And in the lighted palace near
Died the sound of royal cheer;
And they cross'd themselves for fear,
    All the knights at Camelot:
But Lancelot mused a little space;
He said, " She has a lovely face;
God in His mercy lend her grace,
    The Lady of Shalott."
               LORD TENNYSON

LEPANTO

White founts falling in the courts of the sun,
And the Soldan of Byzantium is smiling as they run;
There is laughter like the fountains in that face of all
    men feared,
It stirs the forest darkness, the darkness of his beard,
It curls the blood-red crescent, the crescent of his lips,
For the inmost sea of all the earth is shaken with his
    ships.
They have dared the white republics up the capes of Italy,
They have dashed the Adriatic round the Lion of the Sea,

And the Pope has cast his arms abroad for agony and
    loss,
And called the kings of Christendom for swords about
    the Cross,
The cold queen of England is looking in the glass;
The shadow of the Valois is yawning at the Mass;
From evening isles fantastical rings faint the Spanish gun,
And the Lord upon the Golden Horn is laughing in the
    sun.

Dim drums throbbing, in the hills half heard,
Where only on a nameless throne a crownless prince has
    stirred,
Where, risen from a doubtful seat and half attainted
    stall,
The last knight of Europe takes weapons from the wall,
The last and lingering troubadour to whom the bird has
    sung,
That once went singing southward when all the world
    was young.
In that enormous silence, tiny and unafraid,
Comes up along a winding road the noise of the Crusade.
Strong gongs groaning as the guns boom far,
Don John of Austria is going to the war,
Stiff flags straining in the night-blasts cold
In the gloom black-purple, in the glint old-gold,
Torchlight crimson on the copper kettle-drums,
Then the tuckets, then the trumpets, then the cannon,
    and he comes.
Don John laughing in the brave beard curled,
Spurning of his stirrups like the thrones of all the world,
Holding his head up for a flag of all the free.

Love-light of Spain—hurrah!
Death-light of Africa!
Don John of Austria
Is riding to the sea.

Mahound is in his paradise above the evening star,
(*Don John of Austria is going to the war.*)
He moves a mighty turban on the timeless houri's knees,
His turban that is woven of the sunsets and the seas.
He shakes the peacock gardens as he rises from his ease,
And he strides among the tree-tops and is taller than the
    trees,
And his voice through all the garden is a thunder sent
    to bring
Black Azrael and Ariel and Ammon on the wing.
Giants and the Genii,
Multiplex of wing and eye,
Whose strong obedience broke the sky
When Solomon was king.

They rush in red and purple from the red clouds of the
    morn,
From temples where the yellow gods shut up their eyes
    in scorn;
They rise in green robes roaring from the green hells of
    the sea
Where fallen skies and evil hues and eyeless creatures be;
On them the sea-valves cluster and the grey sea-forests
    curl,
Splashed with a splendid sickness, the sickness of the
    pearl;
They swell in sapphire smoke out of the blue cracks of
    the ground,—

157

They gather and they wonder and give worship to
    Mahound.
And he saith, "Break up the mountains where the
    hermit-folk can hide,
And sift the red and silver sands lest bone of saint abide,
And chase the Giaours flying night and day, not giving
    rest,
For that which was our trouble comes again out of the
    west.
We have set the seal of Solomon on all things under sun,
Of knowledge and of sorrow and endurance of things
    done;
But a noise is in the mountains, in the mountains, and I
    know
The voice that shook our palaces—four hundred years ago:
It is he that saith not 'Kismet'; it is he that knows not
    Fate;
It is Richard, it is Raymond, it is Godfrey in the gate!
It is he whose loss is laughter when he counts the wager
    worth,
Put down your feet upon him, that our peace be on the
    earth."
For he heard drums groaning and he heard guns jar,
(*Don John of Austria is going to the war.*)
Sudden and still—hurrah!
Bolt from Iberia!
Don John of Austria
Is gone by Alcalar.

St. Michael's on his Mountain in the sea-roads of the
    north,
(*Don John of Austria is girt and going forth.*)

Where the grey seas glitter and the sharp tides shift
And the sea-folk labour and the red sails lift.
He shakes his lance of iron and he claps his wings of
    stone;
The noise is gone through Normandy; the noise is gone
    alone;
The North is full of tangled things and texts and aching
    eyes,
And dead is all the innocence of anger and surprise,
And Christian killeth Christian in a narrow dusty
    room,
And Christian dreadeth Christ that hath a newer face
    of doom.
And Christian hateth Mary that God kissed in Galilee,
But Don John of Austria is riding to the sea.
Don John calling through the blast and the eclipse,
Crying with the trumpet, with the trumpet of his lips,
Trumpet that sayeth ha!
Domino gloria!
Don John of Austria
Is shouting to the ships.

King Philip's in his closet with the Fleece about his neck,
(*Don John of Austria is armed upon the deck.*)
The walls are hung with velvet that is black and soft as
    sin,
And little dwarfs creep out of it and little dwarfs creep in.
He holds a crystal phial that has colours like the moon,
He touches, and it tingles, and he trembles very soon,
And his face is as a fungus of a leprous white and grey,
Like plants in the high houses that are shuttered from
    the day,

And death is the phial and the end of noble work,
But Don John of Austria has fired upon the Turk.
Don John's hunting, and his hounds have bayed—
Booms away past Italy the rumour of his raid
Gun upon gun, ha! ha!
Gun upon gun, hurrah!
Don John of Austria
Has loosed the cannonade.

The Pope was in his chapel before day or battle broke,
(*Don John of Austria is hidden in the smoke.*)
The hidden room in man's house where God sits all the
    year,
The secret window whence the world looks small and
    very dear.
He sees as in a mirror on the monstrous twilight sea
The crescent of his cruel ships whose name is mystery;
They fling great shadows foe-wards, making Cross and
    Castle dark,
They veil the plumèd lions on the galleys of St. Mark;
And above the ships are palaces of brown, black-bearded
    chiefs,
And below the ships are prisons, where with multitudi-
    nous griefs,
Christian captives sick and sunless, all a labouring race
    repines
Like a race in sunken cities, like a nation in the
    mines.
They are lost like slaves that swat, and in the skies of
    morning hung
The stairways of the tallest gods when tyranny was
    young.

They are countless, voiceless, hopeless as those fallen or
    fleeing on
Before the high Kings' horses in the granite of Babylon.
And many a one grows witless in his quiet room in hell
Where a yellow face looks inward through the lattice of
    his cell,
And he finds his God forgotten, and he seeks no more a
    sign—
(But Don John of Austria has burst the battle line!)
Don John pounding from the slaughter-painted poop,
Purpling all the ocean like a bloody pirate's sloop,
Scarlet running over on the silvers and the golds,
Breaking of the hatches up and bursting of the holds,
Thronging of the thousands up that labour under sea
White for bliss and blind for sun and stunned for liberty.
Vivat Hispania!
Domino Gloria!
Don John of Austria
Has set his people free!

Cervantes on his galley sets the sword back in the
    sheath,
(Don John of Austria rides homeward with a wreath.)
And he sees across a weary land a straggling road in
    Spain,
Up which a lean and foolish knight forever rides in vain,
And he smiles, but not as Sultans smile, and settles back
    the blade . . .
(But Don John of Austria rides home from the Crusade.)

G. K. CHESTERTON

THE DESTRUCTION OF SENNACHERIB

The Assyrian came down like the wolf on the fold,
And his cohorts were gleaming in purple and gold;
And the sheen of their spears was like stars on the sea,
When the blue wave rolls nightly on deep Galilee.

Like the leaves of the forest when Summer is green,
That host with their banners at sunset were seen:
Like the leaves of the forest when Autumn hath blown,
That host on the morrow lay wither'd and strown.

For the Angel of Death spread his wings on the blast,
And breathed in the face of the foe as he pass'd;
And the eyes of the sleepers wax'd deadly and chill,
And their hearts but once heaved, and for ever grew still!

And there lay the steed with his nostril all wide,
But through it there roll'd not the breath of his pride;
And the foam of his gasping lay white on the turf,
And cold as the spray of the rock-beating surf.

And there lay the rider distorted and pale,
With the dew on his brow, and the rust on his mail:
And the tents were all silent, the banners alone,
The lances unlifted, the trumpet unblown.

And the widows of Ashur are loud in their wail,
And the idols are broke in the temple of Baal;
And the might of the Gentile, unsmote by the sword,
Hath melted like snow in the glance of the Lord!

LORD BYRON

PICTURES FROM LONGER POEMS

SOHRAB MEETS RUSTUM

(From " Sohrab and Rustum ")

The Tartar host is attacking the Persians and Sohrab chal-
lenges the bravest of the Persian lords to meet him in single
combat. Rustum, his father, takes up the challenge and
faces his unknown son.

But Rustum strode to his tent door, and call'd
His followers in, and bade them bring his arms,
And clad himself in steel: the arms he chose
Were plain, and on his shield was no device,
Only his helm was rich, inlaid with gold,
And from the fluted spine atop a plume
Of horsehair wav'd, a scarlet horsehair plume.
So arm'd, he issued forth; and Ruksh, his horse,
Follow'd him, like a faithful hound, at heel—
Ruksh, whose renown was nois'd through all the earth;
The horse, whom Rustum on a foray once
Did in Bokhara by the river find
A colt beneath its dam, and drove him home,
And rear'd him; a bright bay, with lofty crest;
Dight with a saddle-cloth of broider'd green
Crusted with gold, and on the ground were work'd

Bokhara] an ancient city in Asiatic Russia.

All beasts of chase, all beasts which hunters know:
So follow'd, Rustum left his tents, and cross'd
The camp, and to the Persian host appear'd.
And all the Persians knew him, and with shouts
Hail'd; but the Tartars knew not who he was.
And dear as the wet diver to the eyes
Of his pale wife who waits and weeps on shore,
By sandy Bahrein, in the Persian Gulf,
Plunging all day in the blue waves, at night,
Having made up his tale of precious pearls,
Rejoins her in their hut upon the sands—
So dear to the pale Persians Rustum came.

And Rustum to the Persian front advanc'd,
And Sohrab arm'd in Haman's tent, and came.
And as afield the reapers cut a swathe
Down through the middle of a rich man's corn,
And on each side are squares of standing corn,
And in the midst a stubble, short and bare;
So on each side were squares of men, with spears
Bristling, and in the midst, the open sand.
And Rustum came upon the sand, and cast
His eyes towards the Tartar tents, and saw
Sohrab come forth, and eyed him as he came.

As some rich woman, on a winter's morn,
Eyes through her silken curtains the poor drudge
Who with numb blacken'd fingers makes her fire—
At cock-crow, on a starlit winter's morn,
When the frost flowers the whiten'd window panes—
And wonders how she lives, and what the thoughts
Of that poor drudge may be; so Rustum eyed
The unknown adventurous youth, who from afar

Bahrein] an island.

164

Came seeking Rustum, and defying forth
All the most valiant chiefs: long he perus'd
His spirited air, and wonder'd who he was.
For very young he seem'd, tenderly rear'd;
Like some young cypress, tall, and dark, and straight
Which in a queen's secluded garden throws
Its slight dark shadow on the moonlit turf,
By midnight, to a bubbling fountain's sound—
So slender Sohrab seem'd, so softly rear'd.
And a deep pity enter'd Rustum's soul
As he beheld him coming; and he stood,
And beckon'd to him with his hand, and said:—
  "O thou young man, the air of Heaven is soft,
And warm, and pleasant; but the grave is cold.
Heaven's air is better than the cold dead grave.
Behold me: I am vast, and clad in iron,
And tried; and I have stood on many a field
Of blood, and I have fought with many a foe:
Never was that field lost, or that foe sav'd.
O Sohrab, wherefore wilt thou rush on death?
Be govern'd: quit the Tartar host, and come
To Iran, and be as my son to me,
And fight beneath my banner till I die.
There are no youths in Iran brave as thou."
  So he spake, mildly: Sohrab heard his voice,
The mighty voice of Rustum; and he saw
His giant figure planted on the sand,
Sole, like some single tower, which a chief
Has builded on the waste in former years
Against the robbers; and he saw that head,
Streak'd with its first grey hairs: hope fill'd his soul;
And he ran forward and embraced his knees,

And clasp'd his hand within his own, and said:—
   "Oh, by thy father's head! by thine own soul!
Art thou not Rustum? speak! art thou not he?"
   But Rustum ey'd askance the kneeling youth,
And turn'd away, and spoke to his own soul:—
   "Ah me, I muse what this young fox may mean!
False, wily, boastful, are these Tartar boys.
For if I now confess this thing he asks,
And hide it not, but say: *Rustum is here!*
He will not yield indeed, nor quit our foes,
But he will find some pretext not to fight,
And praise my fame, and proffer courteous gifts,
A belt or sword perhaps, and go his way.
And on a feast-tide in Afrasiab's hall,
In Samarcand, he will arise and cry:
'I challenged once, when the two armies camp'd
Beside the Oxus, all the Persian lords
To cope with me in single fight; but they
Shrank, only Rustum dar'd; then he and I
Changed gifts, and went on equal terms away.'
So will he speak, perhaps, while men applaud;
Then were the chiefs of Iran shamed through me."
   And then he turn'd, and sternly spake aloud:—
"Rise! wherefore dost thou vainly question thus
Of Rustum? I am here, whom thou hast call'd
By challenge forth; make good thy vaunt, or yield!
Is it with Rustum only thou wouldst fight?
Rash boy, men look on Rustum's face and flee!
For well I know, that did great Rustum stand
Before thy face this day, and were reveal'd,
There would be then no talk of fighting more.
But being what I am, I tell thee this;

Do thou record it in thine inmost soul:
Either thou shalt renounce thy vaunt, and yield,
Or else thy bones shall strew this sand, till winds
Bleach them, or Oxus with his summer floods,
Oxus in summer wash them all away."

  He spoke: and Sohrab answer'd, on his feet:—
"Art thou so fierce? Thou wilt not fright me so.
I am no girl, to be made pale by words.
Yet this thou hast said well, did Rustum stand
Here on this field, there were no fighting then.
But Rustum is far hence, and we stand here.
Begin: thou art more vast, more dread than I,
And thou art prov'd, I know, and I am young—
But yet success sways with the breath of Heaven.
And though thou thinkest that thou knowest sure
Thy victory, yet thou canst not surely know.
For we are all, like swimmers in the sea,
Pois'd on the top of a huge wave of Fate,
Which hangs uncertain to which side to fall.
And whether it will heave us up to land,
Or whether it will roll us out to sea,
Back out to sea, to the deep waves of death,
We know not, and no search will make us know:
Only the event will teach us in its hour."

  He spoke; and Rustum answer'd not, but hurl'd
His spear; down from the shoulder, down it came,
As on some partridge in the corn a hawk
That long has tower'd in the airy clouds
Drops like a plummet: Sohrab saw it come,
And sprang aside, quick as a flash: the spear
Hiss'd, and went quivering down into the sand,
Which it sent flying wide:—then Sohrab threw

In turn, and full struck Rustum's shield: sharp rang,
The iron plates rang sharp, but turn'd the spear.
And Rustum seiz'd his club, which none but he
Could wield: an unlopp'd trunk it was, and huge,
Still rough; like those which men in treeless plains
To build them boats fish from the flooded rivers,
Hyphasis or Hydaspes, when, high up
By their dark springs, the wind in winter-time
Has made in Himalayan forests wrack,
And strewn the channels with torn boughs—so huge
The club which Rustum lifted now, and struck
One stroke; but again Sohrab sprang aside
Lithe as the glancing snake, and the club came
Thundering to earth, and leapt from Rustum's hand.
And Rustum follow'd his own blow, and fell
To his knees, and with his fingers clutch'd the sand:
And now might Sohrab have unsheath'd his sword,
And pierced the mighty Rustum while he lay
Dizzy, and on his knees, and choked with sand;
But he look'd on, and smil'd, nor bared his sword.
But courteously drew back, and spoke, and said:—
   "Thou strik'st too hard: that club of thine will float
Upon the summer floods, and not my bones.
But rise, and be not wroth; not wroth am I:
No, when I see thee, wrath forsakes my soul.
Thou say'st, thou art not Rustum: be it so!
Who art thou then, that canst so touch my soul?
Boy as I am, I have seen battles too;
Have waded foremost in their bloody waves,
And heard their hollow roar of dying men;
But never was my heart thus touch'd before.
Are they from Heaven, these softenings of the heart?

O thou old warrior, let us yield to Heaven!
Come, plant we here in earth our angry spears,
And make a truce, and sit upon this sand,
And pledge each other in red wine, like friends,
And thou shalt talk to me of Rustum's deeds.
There are enough foes in the Persian host
Whom I may meet, and strike, and feel no pang;
Champions enough Afrasiab has, whom thou
Mayst fight: fight them, when they confront thy spear.
But oh, let there be peace 'twixt thee and me!' "
  He ceased: but while he spake, Rustum had risen,
And stood erect, trembling with rage: his club
He left to lie, but had regain'd his spear,
Whose fiery point now in his mail'd right hand
Blazed bright and baleful, like that autumn Star,
The baleful sign of fevers: dust had soil'd
His stately crest, and dimm'd his glittering arms.
His breast heav'd; his lips foam'd; and twice his voice
Was chok'd with rage: at last these words broke way:—
  " Girl! nimble with thy feet, not with thy hands!
Curl'd minion, dancer, coiner of sweet words!
Fight; let me hear thy hateful voice no more!
Thou art not in Afrasiab's gardens now
With Tartar girls, with whom thou art wont to dance;
But on the Oxus-sands, and in the dance
Of battle, and with me, who make no play
Of war: I fight it out, and hand to hand.
Speak not to me of truce, and pledge, and wine!
Remember all thy valour; try thy feints
And cunning: all the pity I had is gone;
Because thou hast shamed me before both the hosts
With thy light skipping tricks, and thy girl's wiles."

He spoke; and Sohrab kindled at his taunts,
And he too drew his sword: at once they rush'd
Together, as two eagles on one prey
Come rushing down together from the clouds,
One from the east, one from the west: their shields
Dash'd with a clang together, and a din
Rose, such as that the sinewy woodcutters
Make often in the forest's heart at morn,
Of hewing axes, crashing trees—such blows
Rustum and Sohrab on each other hail'd.
And you would say that sun and stars took part
In that unnatural conflict; for a cloud
Grew suddenly in Heaven, and dark'd the sun
Over the fighters' heads; and a wind rose
Under their feet, and moaning swept the plain,
And in a sandy whirlwind wrapp'd the pair.
In gloom they twain were wrapp'd, and they alone;
For both the on-looking hosts on either hand
Stood in broad daylight, and the sky was pure,
And the sun sparkled on the Oxus stream.
But in the gloom they fought, with bloodshot eyes
And labouring breath; first Rustum struck the shield
Which Sohrab held stiff out: the steel-spiked spear
Rent the tough plates, but fail'd to reach the skin,
And Rustum pluck'd it back with angry groan.
Then Sohrab with his sword smote Rustum's helm,
Nor clove its steel quite through; but all the crest
He shore away, and that proud horsehair plume,
Never till now defiled, sunk to the dust;
And Rustum bow'd his head; but then the gloom
Grew blacker: thunder rumbled in the air,
And lightnings rent the cloud; and Ruksh, the horse,

Who stood at hand, utter'd a dreadful cry:
No horse's cry was that, most like the roar
Of some pain'd desert lion, who all day
Has trail'd the hunter's javelin in his side,
And comes at night to die upon the sand.
The two hosts heard that cry, and quaked for fear,
And Oxus curdled as it cross'd his stream.
But Sohrab heard, and quail'd not, but rush'd on,
And struck again; and again Rustum bow'd
His head; but this time all the blade, like glass,
Sprang in a thousand shivers on the helm,
And in his hand the hilt remain'd alone.
Then Rustum rais'd his head: his dreadful eyes
Glared, and he shook on high his menacing spear,
And shouted, *Rustum!* Sohrab heard that shout,
And shrank amazed; back he recoil'd one step,
And scann'd with blinking eyes the advancing form;
And then he stood bewilder'd; and he dropp'd
His covering shield, and the spear pierc'd his side.
He reel'd, and staggering back, sunk to the ground.
And then the gloom dispers'd, and the wind fell,
And the bright sun broke forth, and melted all
The cloud; and the two armies saw the pair;
Saw Rustum standing, safe upon his feet,
And Sohrab, wounded, on the bloody sand.

Then, with a bitter smile, Rustum began: —
" Sohrab, thou thoughtest in thy mind to kill
A Persian lord this day, and strip his corpse,
And bear thy trophies to Afrasiab's tent.
Or else that the great Rustum would come down
Himself to fight, and that thy wiles would move
His heart to take a gift, and let thee go.

And then that all the Tartar host would praise
Thy courage or thy craft, and spread thy fame,
To glad thy father in his weak old age.
Fool! thou art slain, and by an unknown man!
Dearer to the red jackals shalt thou be,
Than to thy friends, and to thy father old."
    And with a fearless mien Sohrab replied:—
"Unknown thou art; yet thy fierce vaunt is vain.
Thou does not slay me, proud and boastful man!
No!   Rustum slays me, and this filial heart.
For were 1 match'd with ten such men as thou,
And I were he who till to-day I was,
They should be lying here, I standing there.
But that belovèd name unnerv'd my arm—
That name, and something, 1 confess, in thee,
Which troubles all my heart, and made my shield
Fall; and thy spear transfix'd an unarm'd foe.
And now thou boastest, and insult'st my fate.
But hear thou this, fierce man, tremble to hear!
The mighty Rustum shall avenge my death!
My father, whom I seek through all the world,
He shall avenge my death, and punish thee! "
    As when some hunter in the spring hath found
A breeding eagle sitting on her nest,
Upon the craggy isle of a hill lake,
And pierced her with an arrow as she rose,
And follow'd her to find her where she fell
Far off;—anon her mate comes winging back
From hunting, and a great way off descries
His huddling young left sole; at that, he checks
His pinion, and with short uneasy sweeps
Circles above his eyry, with loud screams

Chiding his mate back to her nest; but she
Lies dying, with the arrow in her side,
In some far stony gorge out of his ken,
A heap of fluttering feathers—never more
Shall the lake glass her, flying over it;
Never the black and dripping precipices
Echo her stormy scream as she sails by:—
As that poor bird flies home, nor knows his loss,
So Rustum knew not his own loss, but stood
Over his dying son, and knew him not.

   But with a cold, incredulous voice, he said:—
" What prate is this of fathers and revenge?
The mighty Rustum never had a son."

   And, with a failing voice, Sohrab replied:—
" Ah yes, he had! and that lost son am I.
Surely the news will one day reach his ear,
Reach Rustum, where he sits, and tarries long,
Somewhere, I know not where, but far from here;
And pierce him like a stab, and make him leap
To arms, and cry for vengeance upon thee."

MATTHEW ARNOLD

THE OCEAN

(From "Childe Harold's Pilgrimage")

There is a pleasure in the pathless woods,
There is a rapture on the lonely shore,
There is society, where none intrudes,
By the deep Sea, and music in its roar:

I love not Man the less, but Nature more,
From these our interviews, in which I steal
From all I may be, or have been before,
To mingle with the Universe, and feel
What I can ne'er express, yet cannot all conceal.

Roll on, thou deep and dark blue Ocean—roll!
Ten thousand fleets sweep over thee in vain;
Man marks the earth with ruin—his control
Stops with the shore;—upon the watery plain
The wrecks are all thy deed, nor doth remain
A shadow of man's ravage, save his own,
When, for a moment, like a drop of rain,
He sinks into thy depths with bubbling groan,
Without a grave, unknell'd, uncoffin'd, and unknown.

His steps are not upon thy paths,—thy fields
Are not a spoil for him,—thou dost arise
And shake him from thee; the vile strength he wields
For earth's destruction thou dost all despise,
Spurning him from thy bosom to the skies,
And send'st him, shivering in thy playful spray
And howling, to his Gods, where haply lies
His petty hope in some near port or bay,
And dashest him again to earth:—there let him lay.

The armaments which thunderstrike the walls
Of rock-built cities, bidding nations quake,
And monarchs tremble in their capitals,
The oak leviathans, whose huge ribs make
Their clay creator the vain title take
Of lord of thee, and arbiter of war—
These are thy toys, and, as the snowy flake,

They melt into thy yeast of waves, which mar
Alike the Armada's pride or spoils of Trafalgar.

Thy shores are empires, changed in all save thee—
Assyria, Greece, Rome, Carthage, what are they?
Thy waters wash'd them power while they were free,
And many a tyrant since; their shores obey
The stranger, slave, or savage; their decay
Has dried up realms to deserts:—not so thou;—
Unchangeable, save to thy wild waves' play,
Time writes no wrinkle on thine azure brow:
Such as creation's dawn beheld, thou rollest now.

Thou glorious mirror, where the Almighty's form
Glasses itself in tempests; in all time,—
Calm or convulsed, in breeze, or gale, or storm,
Icing the pole, or in the torrid clime
Dark-heaving—boundless, endless, and sublime,
The image of Eternity, the throne
Of the Invisible; even from out thy slime
The monsters of the deep are made; each zone
Obeys thee; thou goest forth, dread, fathomless, alone.

And I have loved thee, Ocean! and my joy
Of youthful sports was on thy breast to be
Borne, like thy bubbles, onward: from a boy
I wanton'd with thy breakers—they to me
Were a delight; and if the freshening sea
Made them a terror—'twas a pleasing fear,
For I was as it were a child of thee,
And trusted to thy billows far and near,
And laid my hand upon thy mane—as I do here.

LORD BYRON

THE POST ARRIVES
(From " The Task ")

Hark! 'tis the twanging horn o'er yonder bridge,
That with its wearisome but needful length
Bestrides the wintry flood, in which the moon
Sees her unwrinkled face reflected bright;
He comes, the herald of a noisy world,
With spatter'd boots, strapp'd waist, and frozen locks:
News from all nations lumb'ring at his back.
True to his charge, the close-pack'd load behind,
Yet careless what he brings, his one concern
Is to conduct it to the destin'd inn:
And, having dropp'd th' expected bag, pass on.
He whistles as he goes, light-hearted wretch,
Cold and yet cheerful: messenger of grief
Perhaps to thousands, and of joy to some;
To him indiff'rent whether grief or joy.
Houses in ashes, and the fall of stocks,
Births, deaths, and marriages, epistles wet
With tears, that trickled down the writer's cheeks
Fast as the periods from his fluent quill,
Or charg'd with am'rous sighs of absent swains,
Or nymphs responsive, equally affect
His horse and him, unconscious of them all.
But oh th' important budget! usher'd in
With such heart-shaking music, who can say
What are its tidings? have our troops awak'd?
Or do they still, as if with opium drugg'd,
Snore to the murmurs of th' Atlantic wave?
Is India free? and does she wear her plum'd

And jewell'd turban with a smile of peace,
Or do we grind her still?   The grand debate,
The popular harangue, the tart reply,
The logic, and the wisdom, and the wit,
And the loud laugh—I long to know them all;
I burn to set th' imprison'd wranglers free,
And give them voice and utt'rance once again.
  Now stir the fire, and close the shutters fast,
Let fall the curtains, wheel the sofa round,
And, while the bubbling and loud-hissing urn
Throws up a steamy column, and the cups,
That cheer but not inebriate, wait on each,
So let us welcome peaceful ev'ning in.
Not such his ev'ning, who with shining face
Sweats in the crowded theatre, and, squeez'd
And bor'd with elbow-points through both his sides,
Out-scolds the ranting actor on the stage:
Nor his, who patient stands till his feet throb,
And his head thumps, to feed upon the breath
Of patriots, bursting with heroic rage,
Or placemen, all tranquillity and smiles.
This folio of four pages, happy work!
Which not ev'n critics criticize; that holds
Inquisitive attention, while I read,
Fast bound in chains of silence, which the fair,
Though eloquent themselves, yet fear to break;
What is it, but a map of busy life,
Its fluctuations, and its vast concerns?

WILLIAM COWPER

THE PARSON

(From " The Deserted Village ")

Near yonder copse, where once the garden smiled,
And still where many a garden-flower grows wild;
There, where a few torn shrubs the place disclose,
The village preacher's modest mansion rose.
A man he was to all the country dear,
And passing rich with forty pounds a year;
Remote from towns he ran his godly race,
Nor e'er had changed, nor wished to change, his place;
Unpractised he to fawn, or seek for power,
By doctrines fashioned to the varying hour;
Far other aims his heart had learned to prize,
More skilled to raise the wretched than to rise.
His house was known to all the vagrant train;
He chid their wanderings, but relieved their pain;
The long-remember'd beggar was his guest,
Whose beard descending swept his agèd breast;
The ruin'd spendthrift, now no longer proud,
Claimed kindred there, and had his claims allowed;
The broken soldier, kindly bade to stay,
Sat by his fire, and talked the night away;
Wept o'er his wounds, or, tales of sorrow done,
Shouldered his crutch, and showed how fields were won.
Pleas'd with his guests, the good man learn'd to glow,
And quite forgot their vices in their woe;
Careless their merits or their faults to scan,
His pity gave ere charity began.

.   .   .   .

At church, with meek and unaffected grace,
His looks adorn'd the venerable place;

Truth from his lips prevailed with double sway,
And fools, who came to scoff, remained to pray.
The service pass'd, around the pious man,
With steady zeal, each honest rustic ran;
E'en children follow'd, with endearing wile,
And plucked his gown, to share the good man's smile
His ready smile a parent's warmth expressed,
Their welfare pleased him, and their cares distressed;
To them his heart, his love, his griefs were giv'n,
But all his serious thoughts had rest in Heaven.
As some tall cliff, that lifts its awful form,
Swells from the vale, and midway leaves the storm,
Though round its breast the rolling clouds are spread,
Eternal sunshine settles on its head.

OLIVER GOLDSMITH

THE SILENT LAKE

(*From " The Prelude "*)

One summer evening (led by her) I found
A little boat tied to a willow tree
Within a rocky cave, its usual home.
Straight I unloosed her chain, and stepping in
Pushed from the shore. It was an act of stealth
And troubled pleasure, nor without the voice
Of mountain-echoes did my boat move on;
Leaving behind her still, on either side,
Small circles glittering idly in the moon,
Until they melted all into one track
Of sparkling light. But now, like one who rows,
Proud of his skill, to reach a chosen point
With an unswerving line, I fixed my view

Upon the summit of a craggy ridge,
The horizon's utmost boundary; far above
Was nothing but the stars and the grey sky.
She was an elfin pinnace; lustily
I dipped my oars into the silent lake,
And, as I rose upon the stroke, my boat
Went heaving through the water like a swan;
When, from behind that craggy steep till then
The horizon's bound, a huge peak, black and huge,
As if with voluntary power instinct
Upreared its head. I struck and struck again,
And growing still in stature the grim shape
Towered up between me and the stars, and still,
For so it seemed, with purpose of its own
And measured motion like a living thing,
Strode after me. With trembling oars I turned,
And through the silent water stole my way
Back to the covert of the willow tree;
There in her mooring-place I left my bark,—
And through the meadows homeward went, in grave
And serious mood; but after I had seen
That spectacle, for many days my brain
Worked with a dim and undetermined sense
Of unknown modes of being; o'er my thoughts
There hung a darkness, call it solitude
Or blank desertion. No familiar shapes
Remained, no pleasant images of trees,
Of sea or sky, no colours of green fields;
But huge and mighty forms, that do not live,
Like living men, moved slowly through the mind
By day, and were a trouble to my dreams.

WILLIAM WORDSWORTH

LYRICS

THE SNARE

I hear a sudden cry of pain!
  There is a rabbit in a snare:
Now I hear the cry again,
  But I cannot tell from where.

But I cannot tell from where
  He is calling out for aid!
Crying on the frightened air,
  Making everything afraid!

Making everything afraid!
  Wrinkling up his little face!
As he cries again for aid;
  And I cannot find the place!

And I cannot find the place
  Where his paw is in the snare!
Little One! Oh, Little One!
  I am searching everywhere!

JAMES STEPHENS

MILK FOR THE CAT

When the tea is brought at five o'clock,
And all the neat curtains are drawn with care,
The little black cat with bright green eyes
Is suddenly purring there.

At first she pretends, having nothing to do,
She has come in merely to blink by the grate.
But, though tea may be late or the milk may be
    sour,
She is never late.

And presently her agate eyes
Take a soft large milky haze,
And her independent casual glance
Becomes a stiff, hard gaze.

Then she stamps her claws or lifts her ears,
Or twists her tail and begins to stir,
Till suddenly all her lithe body becomes
One breathing, trembling purr.

The children eat and wriggle and laugh;
The two old ladies stroke their silk:
But the cat is grown small and thin with desire,
Transformed to a creeping lust for milk.

The white saucer like some full moon descends
At last from the clouds of the table above;
She sighs and dreams and thrills and glows,
Transfigured with love.

She nestles over the shining rim,
Buries her chin in the creamy sea;
Her tail hangs loose; each drowsy paw
Is doubled under each bending knee.

A long dim ecstasy holds her life;
Her world is an infinite shapeless white,
Till her tongue has curled the last holy drop,
Then she sinks back into the night.

Draws and dips her body to heap
Her sleepy nerves in the great arm-chair,
Lies defeated and buried deep
Three or four hours unconscious there.

HAROLD MONRO

THE DONKEY

When fishes flew and forests walked
    And figs grew upon thorn,
Some moment when the moon was blood
    Then surely I was born.

With monstrous head and sickening cry
    And ears like errant wings,
The devil's walking parody
    On all four-footed things.

The tattered outlaw of the earth,
    Of ancient crooked will;
Starve, scourge, deride me: I am dumb,
    I keep my secret still.

183

Fools! For I also had my hour;
    One far fierce hour and sweet:
There was a shout about my ears,
    And palms before my feet.

GILBERT KEITH CHESTERTON

YOU SPOTTED SNAKES WITH DOUBLE TONGUE

(From " A Midsummer Night's Dream ")

You spotted snakes with double tongue,
    Thorny hedgehogs, be not seen;
Newts, and blind-worms, do no wrong:
    Come not near our fairy queen.

    Philomel, with melody,
      Sing in our sweet lullaby;
  Lulla, lulla, lullaby; lulla, lulla, lullaby:
      Never harm,
      Nor spell, nor charm,
    Come our lovely lady nigh:
    So, good night, with lullaby.

Weaving spiders, come not here;
    Hence, you long-legg'd spinners, hence!
Beetles black, approach not near;
    Worm nor snail, do no offence.

    Philomel, with melody,
      Sing in our sweet lullaby;
  Lulla, lulla, lullaby; lulla, lulla, lullaby:

Never harm,
Nor spell nor charm,
Come our lovely lady nigh;
So, good night, with lullaby.

WILLIAM SHAKESPEARE

BLACKBIRD

He comes on chosen evenings,
My blackbird bountiful, and sings
Over the gardens of the town
Just at the hour the sun goes down.
His flight across the chimneys thick,
By some divine arithmetic,
Comes to his customary stack,
And crouches there his plumage black,
And there he lifts his yellow bill
Kindled against the sunset, till
These suburbs are like Dymock woods
Where music has her solitudes,
And while he mocks the winter's wrong
Rapt on his pinnacle of song,
Figured above our garden plots
Those are celestial chimney-pots.

JOHN DRINKWATER

THE KINGFISHER

It was the Rainbow gave thee birth,
And left thee all her lovely hues;

And, as her mother's name was Tears,
  So runs it in my blood to choose
For haunts the lonely pools, and keep
In company with trees that weep.

Go you and, with such glorious hues,
  Live with proud Peacocks in green parks;
On lawns as smooth as shining glass,
Let every feather show its marks;
Get thee on boughs and clap thy wings
Before the windows of proud kings.

Nay, lovely Bird, thou art not vain;
  Thou hast no proud, ambitious mind;
I also love a quiet place
  That's green, away from all mankind;
A lonely pool, and let a tree
Sigh with her bosom over me.

                              WILLIAM HENRY DAVIES

THE WILD DUCK

Twilight. Red in the west.
Dimness. A glow on the wood.
The teams plod home to rest.
The wild duck come to glean.
O souls not understood,
What a wild cry in the pool;
What things have the farm ducks seen
That they cry so—huddle and cry?

Only the soul that goes.
Eager.   Eager.   Flying.
Over the globe of the moon,
Over the wood that glows.
Wings linked.   Necks a-strain,
A rush and a wild crying.

.   .   .   .   .

A cry of the long pain
In the reeds of a steel lagoon,
In a land that no man knows.

JOHN MASEFIELD

TO THE CUCKOO

O blithe New-comer!   I have heard,
I hear thee and rejoice.
O Cuckoo! shall I call thee Bird,
Or but a wandering Voice?

While I am lying on the grass
Thy twofold shout I hear;
From hill to hill it seems to pass,
At once far off, and near.

Though babbling only to the Vale,
Of sunshine and of flowers,
Thou bringest unto me a tale
Of visionary hours.

Thrice welcome, darling of the Spring!
Even yet thou art to me
No bird, but an invisible thing,
A voice, a mystery;

The same whom in my schoolboy days
I listened to; that Cry
Which made me look a thousand ways
In bush, and tree, and sky.

To seek thee did I often rove
Through woods and on the green;
And thou wert still a hope, a love;
Still longed for, never seen.

And I can listen to thee yet;
Can lie upon the plain
And listen, till I do beget
That golden time again.

O blessèd Bird! the earth we pace
Again appears to be
An unsubstantial, faery place,
That is fit home for Thee!

WILLIAM WORDSWORTH

WEATHERS

This is the weather the cuckoo likes,
    And so do I;
When showers betumble the chestnut spikes,
    And nestlings fly:
And the little brown nightingale bills his best,
And they sit outside at "The Travellers' Rest,"
And maids come forth sprig-muslin drest,
And citizens dream of the south and west,
    And so do I.

This is the weather the shepherd shuns,
    And so do I;
When beeches drip on browns and duns,
    And thresh, and ply;
And hill-hid tides throb, throe on throe,
And meadow rivulets overflow,
And drops on gate-bars hang in a row,
And rooks in families homeward go,
    And so do I.

THOMAS HARDY

A WINDY DAY

This wind brings all dead things to life,
Branches that lash the air like whips
And dead leaves rolling in a hurry
Or peering in a rabbits' bury
Or trying to push down a tree;
Gates that fly open to the wind
And close again behind,
And fields that are a flowing sea
And make the cattle look like ships;
Straws glistening and stiff
Lying on air as on a shelf
And pond that leaps to leave itself;
And feathers too that rise and float,
Each feather changed into a bird,
And line-hung sheets that crack and strain;
Even the sun-greened coat,
That through so many winds has served,
The scarecrow struggles to put on again.

ANDREW YOUNG

189

SHELLEY

THE CLOUD

I bring fresh showers for the thirsting flowers,
    From the seas and the streams;
I bear light shade for the leaves when laid
    In their noonday dreams.
From my wings are shaken the dews that waken
    The sweet buds every one,
When rocked to rest on their mother's breast,
    As she dances about the sun.
I wield the flail of the lashing hail,
    And whiten the green plains under,
And then again I dissolve it in rain,
    And laugh as I pass in thunder.

I sift the snow on the mountains below,
    And their great pines groan aghast;
And all the night 'tis my pillow white,
    While I sleep in the arms of the blast.
Sublime on the towers of my skiey bowers,
    Lightning my pilot sits;
In a cavern under is fettered the thunder,
    It struggles and howls at fits;
Over earth and ocean, with gentle motion,
    This pilot is guiding me,
Lured by the love of the genii that move
    In the depths of the purple sea;
Over the rills, and the crags, and the hills,
    Over the lakes and the plains,
Wherever he dream, under mountain or stream,
    The Spirit he loves remains;

And I all the while bask in Heaven's blue smile,
    Whilst he is dissolving in rains.

The sanguine Sunrise, with his meteor eyes,
    And his burning plumes outspread,
Leaps on the back of my sailing rack,
    When the morning star shines dead;
As on the jag of a mountain crag,
    Which an earthquake rocks and swings,
An eagle alit one moment may sit
    In the light of its golden wings.
And when Sunset may breathe, from the lit sea beneath,
    Its ardours of rest and of love,
And the crimson pall of eve may fall
    From the depth of Heaven above,
With wings folded I rest, on mine aëry nest,
    As still as a brooding dove.

That orbèd maiden with white fire laden,
    Whom mortals call the Moon,
Glides glimmering o'er my fleece-like floor,
    By the midnight breezes strewn;
And wherever the beat of her unseen feet,
    Which only the angels hear,
May have broken the woof of my tent's thin roof,
    The stars peep behind her and peer;
And I laugh to see them whirl and flee,
    Like a swarm of golden bees,
When I widen the rent in my wind-built tent,
    Till the calm rivers, lakes, and seas,
Like strips of the sky fallen through me on high,
    Are each paved with the moon and these.

I bind the Sun's throne with a burning zone,
    And the Moon's with a girdle of pearl;
The volcanoes are dim, and the stars reel and swim,
    When the whirlwinds my banner unfurl.
From cape to cape, with a bridge-like shape,
    Over a torrent sea,
Sunbeam-proof, I hang like a roof,—
    The mountains its columns be.
The triumphal arch through which I march
    With hurricane, fire, and snow,
When the Powers of the air are chained to my chair,
    Is the million-coloured bow;
The sphere-fire above its soft colours wove,
    While the moist Earth was laughing below.

I am the daughter of Earth and Water,
    And the nursling of the Sky;
I pass through the pores of the ocean and shores;
    I change, but I cannot die.
For after the rain when with never a stain
    The pavilion of Heaven is bare,
And the winds and sunbeams with their convex gleams
    Build up the blue dome of air,
I silently laugh at my own cenotaph,
    And out of the caverns of rain,
Like a child from the womb, like a ghost from the tomb,
    I arise and unbuild it again.

PERCY BYSSHE SHELLEY

THE STREAM'S SONG

Make way, make way,
You thwarting stones;
Room for my play,
Serious ones.

Do you not fear,
O rocks and boulders,
To feel my laughter
On your grave shoulders?

Do you not know
My joy at length
Will all wear out
Your solemn strength?

You will not for ever
Cumber my play;
With joy and a song
I clear my way.

Your faith of rock
Shall yield to me,
And be carried away
By the song of my glee.

Crumble, crumble,
Voiceless things;
No faith can last
That never sings.

For the last hour
To joy belongs;
The steadfast perish,
But not the songs.

Yet for a while
Thwart me, O boulders;
I need for laughter
Your serious shoulders.

And when my singing
Has razed you quite,
I shall have lost
Half my delight.

LASCELLES ABERCROMBIE

THE SOLITARY REAPER

Behold her, single in the field,
  Yon solitary Highland Lass!
Reaping and singing by herself;
  Stop here, or gently pass!
Alone she cuts and binds the grain,
And sings a melancholy strain;
O listen! for the Vale profound
Is overflowing with the sound.

No Nightingale did ever chaunt
  More welcome notes to weary bands
Of travellers in some shady haunt,
  Among Arabian sands:

194

A voice so thrilling ne'er was heard
In spring-time from the Cuckoo-bird,
Breaking the silence of the seas
Among the farthest Hebrides.

Will no one tell me what she sings?—
    Perhaps the plaintive numbers flow
For old, unhappy, far-off things,
    And battles long ago:
Or is it some more humble lay,
Familiar matter of to-day?
Some natural sorrow, loss, or pain,
That has been, and may be again?

Whate'er the theme, the Maiden sang
    As if her song could have no ending;
I saw her singing at her work,
    And o'er the sickle bending;—
I listen'd, motionless and still;
And, as I mounted up the hill,
The music in my heart I bore,
Long after it was heard no more.

WILLIAM WORDSWORTH

A MAN'S A MAN FOR A' THAT

Is there, for honest poverty,
    That hangs his head, and a' that?
The coward-slave, we pass him by,
    We dare be poor for a' that!
For a' that, and a' that,
    Our toil's obscure, and a' that;

The rank is but the guinea-stamp,
  The man's the gowd for a' that.

What though on hamely fare we dine,
  Wear hodden grey, and a' that;
Gie fools their silks, and knaves their wine,
  A man's a man for a' that!
For a' that, and a' that,
  Their tinsel show, and a' that;
The honest man, though e'er sae poor,
  Is king o' men for a' that.

You see yon birkie, ca'd a lord,
  Wha struts, and stares, and a' that;
Though hundreds worship at his word,
  He's but a coof for a' that:
For a' that, and a' that,
  His riband, star and a' that;
The man of independent mind,
  He looks and laughs at a' that.

A king can mak' a belted knight,
  A marquis, duke, and a' that;
But an honest man's aboon his might,
  Guid faith he mauna fa' that!
For a' that, and a' that,
  Their dignities, and a' that,
The pith o' sense, and pride o' worth,
  Are higher rank than a' that.

Then let us pray that come it may—
  As come it will, for a' that—
That sense and worth, o'er a' the earth,
  May bear the gree, and a' that;

For a' that, and a' that,
    It's comin' yet for a' that,
That man to man, the warld o'er,
    Shall brothers be for a' that!

ROBERT BURNS

hodden grey] coarse woollen cloth.   coof] stupid fellow.
            bear the gree] carry off the prize.

RICH DAYS

Welcome to you rich Autumn days,
    Ere comes the cold, leaf-picking wind;
When golden stooks are seen in fields,
    All standing arm-in-arm entwined;
And gallons of sweet cider seen
On trees in apples red and green.

With mellow pears that cheat our teeth,
    Which melt that tongues may suck them in;
With cherries red, and blue-black plums,
    Now sweet and soft from stone to skin;
And woodnuts rich, to make us go
Into the loveliest lanes we know.

WILLIAM HENRY DAVIES

ODE TO THE NORTH-EAST WIND

Welcome, wild North-easter!
    Shame it is to see
Odes to every zephyr;
    Ne'er a verse to thee.

197

Welcome, black North-easter!
　O'er the German foam,
O'er the Danish moorlands,
　From thy frozen home.
Tired we are of summer,
　Tired of gaudy glare,
Showers soft and steaming,
　Hot and breathless air.
Tired of listless dreaming,
　Through the lazy day:
Jovial wind of winter
　Turn us out to play!
Sweep the golden reed-beds;
　Crisp the lazy dyke;
Hunger into madness
　Every plunging pike.
Fill the lake with wild-fowl;
　Fill the marsh with snipe;
While on dreary moorlands
　Lonely curlew pipe.
Through the black fir-forest
　Thunder harsh and dry,
Shattering down the snow-flakes
　Off the curdled sky.
Hark! The brave North-easter!
　Breast-high lies the scent,
On by holt and headland,
　Over heath and bent.
Chime, ye dappled darlings,
　Through the sleet and snow.

　　holt] wood.
　　bent] stiff, grass-like reeds.

Who can over-ride you?
    Let the horses go!
Chime, ye dappled darlings,
    Down the roaring blast;
You shall see a fox die
    Ere an hour be past.
Go! and rest to-morrow,
    Hunting in your dreams,
While our skates are ringing
    O'er the frozen streams.
Let the luscious South-wind
    Breathe in lovers' sighs,
While the lazy gallants
    Bask in ladies' eyes.
What does he but soften
    Heart alike and pen?
'Tis the hard grey weather
    Breeds hard English men.
What's the soft South-wester?
    'Tis the ladies' breeze,
Bringing home their true loves
    Out of all the seas:
But the black North-easter,
    Through the snowstorm hurled,
Drives our English hearts of oak
    Seaward round the world.
Come, as came our fathers,
    Heralded by thee,
Conquering from the eastward,
    Lords by land and sea.
Come; and strong within us
    Stir the Vikings' blood;

Bracing brain and sinew;
Blow, thou wind of God!

CHARLES KINGSLEY

OLD WINTER

Old Winter, sad, in snow yclad,
    Is making a doleful din;
But let him howl till he crack his jowl,
    We will not let him in.

Ay, let him lift from the billowy drift
    His hoary, haggard form,
And scowling stand, with his wrinkled hand
    Outstretching to the storm.

And let his weird and sleety beard
    Stream loose upon the blast,
And, rustling, chime to the tinkling rime
    From his bald head falling fast.

Let his baleful breath shed blight and death
    On herb and flower and tree;
And brooks and ponds in crystal bonds
    Bind fast, but what care we?

Let him push at the door, in the chimney roar.
    And rattle the window pane;
Let him in at us spy with his icicle eye,
    But he shall not entrance gain.

Let him gnaw, forsooth, with his freezing tooth,
   On our roof-tiles, till he tire;
But we care not a whit, as we jovial sit
   Before our blazing fire.

Come, lads, let's sing, till the rafters ring;
   Come push the can about—
From our snug fireside this Christmas-tide
   We'll keep old Winter out.

T. NOEL

UNDER THE GREENWOOD TREE

(From " As You Like It ")

Under the greenwood tree,
Who loves to lie with me,
And turn his merry note
Unto the sweet bird's throat,
Come hither, come hither, come hither:
   Here shall he see
   No enemy
But winter and rough weather.

Who doth ambition shun,
And loves to live i' the sun.
Seeking the food he eats,
And pleased with what he gets,
Come hither, come hither, come hither:
   Here shall he see
   No enemy
But winter and rough weather.

WILLIAM SHAKESPEARE

THE HILL

Breathless, we flung us on the windy hill,
　　Laughed in the sun, and kissed the lovely grass.
　　You said, "Through glory and ecstasy we pass;
Wind, sun, and earth remain, the birds sing still,
When we are old, are old . . ." " And when we die
　　All's over that is ours; and life burns on
Through other lovers, other lips," said I,
　　" Heart of my heart, our heaven is now, is won! "

" We are Earth's best, that learnt her lesson here.
　　Life is our cry.　We have kept the faith! " we said;
　　" We shall go down with unreluctant tread
Rose-crowned into the darkness! "—Proud we were,
And laughed, that had such brave true things to say.
—And then you suddenly cried, and turned away.

RUPERT BROOKE

CORRYMEELA

Over here in England I'm helpin' wi' the hay,
　　An' I wisht I was in Ireland the livelong day;
Weary on the English hay, an' sorra take the wheat!
　　Och!　Corrymeela an' the blue sky over it.

There's a deep dumb river flowin' by beyont the heavy
　　　trees,
　　This livin' air is moithered wi' the bummin' o' the
　　　bees;

202

I wisht I'd hear the Claddagh burn go runnin' through
    the heat
    Past Corrymeela, wi' the blue sky over it.

The people that's in England is richer nor the Jews,
    There not the smallest young gossoon but thravels in
    his shoes!
I'd give the pipe between me teeth to see a barefut child,
    Och! Corrymeela an' the low south wind.

Here's hands so full o' money an' hearts so full o' care,
    By the luck o' love! I'd still go light for all I did go
    bare.
"God save ye, *colleen dhas*," I said: the girl she thought
    me wild.
    Far Corrymeela, an' the low south wind.

D'ye mind me now, the song at night is mortial hard to
    raise,
    The girls are heavy goin' here, the boys are ill to plase;
When one'st I'm out this workin' hive, 'tis I'll be back
    again—
    Ay, Corrymeela, in the same soft rain.

The puff o' smoke from one ould roof before an English
    town!
    For a *shaugh* wid Andy Feelan here I'd give a silver
    crown,
For a curl o' hair like Mollie's ye'll ask the like in vain,
    Sweet Corrymeela, an' the same soft rain.

MOIRA O'NEILL

203

BLOW, BLOW, THOU WINTER WIND

(From " As You Like It ")

Blow, blow, thou winter wind,
Thou art not so unkind
 As man's ingratitude;
Thy tooth is not so keen,
Because thou art not seen,
 Although thy breath be rude.
Heigh-ho! sing, heigh-ho! unto the green holly:
Most friendship is feigning, most loving mere folly:
 Then heigh-ho, the holly!
 This life is most jolly.

Freeze, freeze, thou bitter sky,
That dost not bite so nigh
 As benefits forgot:
Though thou the waters warp,
Thy sting is not so sharp
 As friend remember'd not.
Heigh-ho! sing, heigh-ho! unto the green holly:
Most friendship is feigning, most loving mere folly:
 Then heigh-ho, the holly!
 This life is most jolly.

WILLIAM SHAKESPEARE

warp] to shrivel or wrinkle through shrinkage in cold weather.

THE MIDNIGHT SKATERS

The hop-poles stand in cones,
 The icy pond lurks under,

The pole-tops steeple to the thrones
  Of stars, sound gulfs of wonder;
But not the tallest there, 'tis said,
Could fathom to this pond's black bed.

Then is not death at watch
  Within those secret waters?
What wants he but to catch
  Earth's heedless sons and daughters?
With but a crystal parapet
Between, he has his engines set.

Then on, blood shouts, on, on,
  Twirl, wheel and whip above him,
Dance on this ball-floor thin and wan,
  Use him as though you love him;
Court him, elude him, reel and pass,
And let him hate you through the glass.

EDMUND BLUNDEN

THE OXEN

Christmas Eve, and twelve of the clock,
  " Now they are all on their knees,"
An elder said as we sat in a flock
  By the embers in hearthside ease.

We pictured the meek mild creatures where
  They dwelt in their strawy pen,
Nor did it occur to one of us there
  To doubt they were kneeling then.

So fair a fancy few would weave
  In these years! Yet, I feel,
If some one said on Christmas Eve,
  "Come; see the oxen kneel

"In the lonely barton by yonder coomb
  Our childhood used to know,"
I should go with him in the gloom,
  Hoping it might be so.

THOMAS HARDY

WHEN ICICLES HANG BY THE WALL
(*From " Love's Labour's Lost "*)

When icicles hang by the wall,
  And Dick the shepherd blows his nail,
And Tom bears logs into the hall,
  And milk comes frozen home in pail,
When blood is nipped and ways be foul,
When nightly sings the staring owl,
                                    To-whit!
      To-who!—a merry note,
While greasy Joan doth keel the pot.

When all aloud the wind doth blow,
  And coughing drowns the parson's saw,
And birds sit brooding in the snow,
  And Marian's nose looks red and raw,
When roasted crabs hiss in the bowl,
When nightly sings the staring owl,
                                    To-whit!

To-who!—a merry note,
While greasy Joan doth keel the pot.

WILLIAM SHAKESPEARE

keel] to cool by stirring or skimming.   saw] wise saying.
crabs] crab apples.

SPRING IS COMING

The spring is coming by many a sign;
The trays are up, the hedges broken down,
That fenced the haystack, and the remnant shines
Like some old antique fragment weather'd brown.
And where suns peep, in every shelter'd place,
The little early buttercups unfold
A glittering star or two—till many trace
The edges of the blackthorn clumps in gold.
And then a little lamb bolts up behind
The hill and wags his tail to meet the yoe;
And then another, shelter'd from the wind,
Lies all his length as dead—and lets me go
Close by and never stirs, but beaking lies,
With legs stretch'd out as though he could not rise.

JOHN CLARE

tray] feeding trough or large hurdle.   yoe] ewe.   beaking] basking.

TO DAFFODILS

Fair daffodils, we weep to see
You haste away so soon:
As yet the early-rising sun
Has not attain'd his noon,

Stay, stay,
Until the hasting day
Has run
But to the even-song;
And, having pray'd together, we
Will go with you along.

We have short time to stay, as you,
We have as short a spring;
As quick a growth to meet decay,
As you, or any thing.
We die,
As your hours do, and dry
Away,
Like to the summer's rain;
Or as the pearls of morning's dew
Ne'er to be found again.

ROBERT HERRICK

THE DAFFODILS

I wandered lonely as a cloud
That floats on high o'er vales and hills,
When all at once I saw a crowd,
A host, of golden daffodils;
Beside the lake, beneath the trees,
Fluttering and dancing in the breeze.

Continuous as the stars that shine
And twinkle on the milky way,
They stretched in never-ending line
Along the margin of a bay:
Ten thousand saw I at a glance
Tossing their heads in sprightly dance.

The waves beside them danced; but they
    Out-did the sparkling waves in glee:
A Poet could not but be gay
    In such a jocund company:
I gazed—and gazed—but little thought
What wealth the show to me had brought:

For oft, when on my couch I lie
    In vacant or in pensive mood,
They flash upon that inward eye
    Which is the bliss of solitude;
And then my heart with pleasure fills,
And dances with the daffodils.

WILLIAM WORDSWORTH

TO A MOUNTAIN DAISY

On turning one down with the Plough, in April, 1786

Wee, modest, crimson-tippèd flow'r,
Thou's met me in an evil hour;
For I maun crush amang the stoure
       Thy slender stem:
To spare thee now is past my pow'r,
       Thou bonnie gem.

Alas! it's no thy neibor sweet,
The bonnie lark, companion meet,
Bending thee 'mang the dewy weet
       Wi' spreckl'd breast,
When upward springing, blythe, to greet
       The purpling east.

Cauld blew the bitter-biting north
Upon thy early, humble birth;
Yet cheerfully thou glinted forth
      Amid the storm,
Scarce rear'd above the parent-earth
      Thy tender form.

The flaunting flow'rs our gardens yield
High shelt'ring woods and wa's maun shield,
But thou, beneath the random bield
      O' clod or stane,
Adorns the histie stibble-field,
      Unseen, alane.

There, in thy scanty mantle clad,
Thy snawy bosom sun-ward spread,
Thou lifts thy unassuming head
      In humble guise;
But now the share uptears thy bed,
      And low thou lies!

ROBERT BURNS

stoure] dust.   bield] shelter.   histie] dry.

THE MOUNTAIN DAISY

So fair, so sweet, withal so sensitive,
Would that the little Flowers were born to live,
Conscious of half the pleasure which they give;

That to this mountain-daisy's self were known
The beauty of its star-shaped shadow, thrown
On the smooth surface of this naked stone!

And what if hence a bold desire should mount
High as the Sun, that he could take account
Of all that issues from his glorious fount!

So might he ken how by his sovereign aid
These delicate companionships are made;
And how he rules the pomp of light and shade;

And were the Sister-power that shines by night
So privileged, what a countenance of delight
Would through the clouds break forth on human
    sight!

Fond fancies! wheresoe'er shall turn thine eye
On earth, air, ocean, or the starry sky,
Converse with Nature in pure sympathy;

All vain desires, all lawless wishes quelled,
Be Thou to love and praise alike impelled,
Whatever boon is granted or withheld.

WILLIAM WORDSWORTH

HOME-THOUGHTS FROM ABROAD

Oh, to be in England
Now that April's there,
And whoever wakes in England
Sees, some morning, unaware,
That the lowest boughs and the brushwood sheaf
Round the elm-tree bole are in tiny leaf,
While the chaffinch sings on the orchard bough
In England—now!

And after April, when May follows,
And the whitethroat builds, and all the swallows!
Hark, where my blossomed pear-tree in the hedge
Leans to the field and scatters on the clover
Blossoms and dewdrops—at the bent spray's edge—
That's the wise thrush; he sings each song twice over,
Lest you should think he never could recapture
The first fine careless rapture!
And though the fields look rough with hoary dew,
All will be gay when noontide wakes anew
The buttercups, the little children's dower
—Far brighter than this gaudy melon-flower!

ROBERT BROWNING

THE VAGABOND

(TO AN AIR OF SCHUBERT)

Give to me the life I love,
  Let the lave go by me,
Give the jolly heaven above
  And the byway nigh me.
Bed in the bush with stars to see,
  Bread I dip in the river—
There's the life for a man like me,
  There's the life for ever.

Let the blow fall soon or late,
  Let what will be o'er me;
Give the face of earth around
  And the road before me.

Wealth I seek not, hope nor love,
  Nor a friend to know me;
All I seek, the heaven above
  And the road below me.

Or let autumn fall on me
  Where afield I linger,
Silencing the bird on tree,
  Biting the blue finger:
White as meal the frosty field—
  Warm the fireside haven—
Not to autumn will I yield,
  Not to winter even!

Let the blow fall soon or late,
  Let what will be o'er me;
Give the face of earth around
  And the road before me.
Wealth I ask not, hope nor love,
  Nor a friend to know me.
All I ask, the heaven above,
  And the road below me.

ROBERT LOUIS STEVENSON

THE VAGABOND

I know the pools where the grayling rise,
  I know the trees where the filberts fall,
I know the woods where the red fox lies,
  The twisted elms where the brown owls call.

213

And I've seldom a shilling to call my own,
  And there's never a girl I'd marry,
I thank the Lord I am a rolling stone
  With never a care to carry.

I talk to the stars as they come and go
  On every night from July to June,
I'm free of the speech of the winds that blow,
  And I know what weather will sing what tune
I sow no seed and I pay no rent,
  And I thank no man for his bounties,
But I've a treasure that's never spent,
  I'm lord of a dozen counties.

JOHN DRINKWATER

MEG MERRILIES

Old Meg she was a Gipsy,
  And liv'd upon the Moors:
Her bed it was the brown heath turf,
  And her house was out of doors.

Her apples were swart blackberries,
  Her currants, pods o' broom;
Her wine was dew of the wild white rose,
  Her book a churchyard tomb.

Her Brothers were the craggy hills,
  Her Sisters larchen trees—
Alone with her great family
  She liv'd as she did please.

No breakfast had she many a morn,
    No dinner many a noon,
And 'stead of supper she would stare
    Full hard against the Moon.

But every morn of woodbine fresh
    She made her garlanding,
And every night the dark glen Yew
    She wove, and she would sing.

And with her fingers old and brown
    She plaited Mats o' Rushes,
And gave them to the Cottagers
    She met among the Bushes.

Old Meg was brave as Margaret Queen
    And tall as Amazon:
An old red blanket cloak she wore;
    A chip-hat had she on.
God rest her agèd bones somewhere—
    She died full long agone!

JOHN KEATS

chip-hat] a hat made of thin strips of woody fibre.

THE JOYS OF THE ROAD

Now the joys of the road are chiefly these:
A crimson touch on the hard-wood trees;

A vagrant's morning wide and blue,
In early fall, when the wind walks, too;

A shadowy highway cool and brown,
Alluring up and enticing down

From rippled water to dappled swamp,
From purple glory to scarlet pomp;

The outward eye, the quiet will,
And the striding heart from hill to hill;

The tempter apple over the fence;
The cobweb bloom on the yellow quince;

The palish asters along the wood,—
A lyric touch of the solitude;

An open hand, an easy shoe,
And a hope to make the day go through,—

Another to sleep with, and a third
To wake me up at the voice of a bird,

The resonant far-listening morn,
And the hoarse whisper of the corn;

The crickets mourning their comrades lost,
In the night's retreat from the gathering frost;

(Or is it their slogan, plaintive and shrill,
As they beat on their corselets, valiant still?)

A hunger fit for the kings of the sea,
And a loaf of bread for Dickon and me;

A thirst like that of the Thirsty Sword,
And a jug of cider on the board;

An idle noon, a bubbling spring,
The sea in the pine-tops murmuring;

A scrap of gossip at the ferry;
A comrade neither glum nor merry,

Asking nothing, revealing naught,
But minting his words from a fund of thought,

A keeper of silence eloquent,
Needy, yet royally well content,

Of the mettled breed, yet abhorring strife,
And full of the mellow juice of life,

A taster of wine, with an eye for a maid,
Never too bold, and never afraid,

Never heart-whole, never heart-sick,
(These are the things I worship in Dick)

No fidget and no reformer, just
A calm observer of ought and must,

A lover of books, but a reader of man,
No cynic and no charlatan,

Who never defers and never demands,
But, smiling, takes the world in his hands,—

Seeing it good as when God first saw
And gave it the weight of His will for law,

And O the joy that is never won,
But follows and follows the journeying sun,

By marsh and tide, by meadow and stream,
A will-o'-the-wind, a light-o'-dream,

Delusion afar, delight anear,
From morrow to morrow, from year to year.

A jack-o'-lantern, a fairy fire,
A dare, a bliss, and a desire!

The racy smell of the forest loam,
When the stealthy, sad-heart leaves go home:

(O leaves, O leaves, I am one with you,
Of the mould and the sun and the wind and the
    dew!)

The broad gold wake of the afternoon;
The silent fleck of the cold new moon;

The sound of the hollow sea's release
From stormy tumult to starry peace;

With only another league to wend;
And two brown arms at the journey's end!

These are the joys of the open road—
For him who travels without a load.

BLISS CARMAN

TIME, YOU OLD GIPSY MAN

Time, you old gipsy man,
Will you not stay,
Put up your caravan
   Just for one day?

All things I'll give you
Will you be my guest,
Bells for your jennet
Of silver the best,
Goldsmiths shall beat you
A great golden ring,
Peacocks shall bow to you,
Little boys sing,
Oh, and sweet girls will
Festoon you with may,
Time, you old gipsy,
Why hasten away?

Last week in Babylon,
Last night in Rome,
Morning, and in the crush
Under Paul's dome;
Under Paul's dial
You tighten your rein—
Only a moment,
And off once again;
Off to some city
Now blind in the womb,
Off to another
Ere that's in the tomb.

> Time, you old gipsy man,
>   Will you not stay,
> Put up your caravan
>   Just for one day?

RALPH HODGSON

ROMANCE

I will make you brooches and toys for your delight
Of bird-song at morning and star-shine at night.
I will make a palace fit for you and me,
Of green days in forests and blue days at sea.

I will make my kitchen, and you shall keep your room,
Where white flows the river and bright blows the broom,
And you shall wash your linen and keep your body white
In rainfall at morning and dewfall at night.

And this shall be for music when no one else is near,
The fine song for singing, the rare song to hear!
That only I remember, that only you admire,
Of the broad road that stretches and the roadside fire.

ROBERT LOUIS STEVENSON

AN OLD WOMAN OF THE ROADS

O, to have a little house!
To own the hearth and stool and all!
The heap'd-up sods upon the fire,
The pile of turf against the wall!

To have a clock with weights and chains
And pendulum swinging up and down!
A dresser filled with shining delph,
Speckled and white and blue and brown!

I could be busy all the day
Clearing and sweeping hearth and floor;
And fixing on their shelf again
My white and blue and speckled store!

I could be quiet there at night
Beside the fire and by myself,
Sure of a bed and loth to leave
The ticking clock and the shining delph!

Och! but I'm weary of mist and dark,
And roads where there's never a house nor bush,
And tired I am of bog and road
And the crying wind and the lonesome hush!

And I am praying to God on high,
And I am praying Him night and day,
For a little house—a house of my own—
Out of the wind's and the rain's way.

PADRAIC COLUM

THE LAKE ISLE OF INNISFREE

I will arise and go now, and go to Innisfree,
And a small cabin build there, of clay and wattles made:
Nine bean rows will I have there, a hive for the honey
    bee,
    And live alone in the bee-loud glade.

And I shall have some peace there, for peace comes drop-
  ping slow,
Dropping from the veils of the morning to where the
  cricket sings;
There midnight's all a-glimmer, and noon a purple glow,
  And evening full of the linnet's wings.

I will arise and go now, for always night and day
I hear lake water lapping with low sounds by the shore;
While I stand on the roadway, or on the pavements gray,
  I hear it in the deep heart's core.

WILLIAM BUTLER YEATS

IN MERCER STREET

I

A PIPER

A piper in the streets to-day
Set up, and tuned, and started to play,
And away, away, away on the tide
Of his music we started; on every side
Doors and windows were opened wide,
And men left down their work and came,
And women with petticoats coloured like flame
And little bare feet that were blue with cold,
Went dancing back to the age of gold,
And all the world went gay, went gay,
For half an hour in the street to-day.

II
RAGS AND BONES

Gather 'em, gather 'em, gather 'em O,
He shouts monotonous, jolting slow
His little truck of rags and bones
Over the uneven cobble stones.
Ever about him cling and crowd
The waifs, a many-coloured cloud
All shrilly clamouring, mad with joy,
For sticky sweet, or painted toy.
Hardly a breath is in the air,
Yet every little windmill there
Goes whirling wildly, as though it knew
With every turn what rapture flew
Through all the heavy street, and stirred
The stagnant air, till the sad bird,
High on the wall, takes heart to sing
And hails the simulated Spring.

III
THE LARK'S SONG

In Mercer Street the light slants down,
And straightway an enchanted town
Is round him, pinnacle and spire
Flash back, elate, the sudden fire;
And clear above the silent street
Falls suddenly and strangely sweet
The lark's song. Bubbling, note on note
Rise fountain-like, o'erflow and float
Tide upon tide, and make more fair
The magic of the sunlit air.

No more the cage can do him wrong,
All is forgotten save his song;
He has forgot the ways of men,
Wide heaven is over him again,
And round him the wide fields of dew
That his first infant mornings knew,
E'er yet the dolorous years had brought
The hours of captive anguish, fraught
With the vile clamour of the street,
The insult of the passing feet,
The torture of the daily round,
The organ's blasphemy of sound.
Sudden some old swift memory brings
The knowledge of forgotten wings,
He springs elate and panting falls
At the rude touch of prison walls.
Silence. Again the street is grey;
Shut down the windows—Work-a-day.

SEUMAS O'SULLIVAN

THE LISTENERS

" Is there anybody there? " said the Traveller,
    Knocking on the moonlit door;
And his horse in the silence champ'd the grasses
    Of the forest's ferny floor:
And a bird flew up out of the turret,
    Above the Traveller's head:
And he smote upon the door again a second time;
    " Is there anybody there? " he said.

But no one descended to the Traveller;
　No head from the leaf-fringed sill
Lean'd over and look'd into his grey eyes,
　Where he stood perplex'd and still.
But only a host of phantom listeners
　That dwelt in the lone house then
Stood listening in the quiet of the moonlight
　To that voice from the world of men:
Stood thronging the faint moonbeams on the dark stair,
　That goes down to the empty hall,
Hearkening in an air stirr'd and shaken
　By the lonely Traveller's call.
And he felt in his heart their strangeness,
　Their stillness answering his cry,
While his horse moved, cropping the dark turf,
　'Neath the starred and leafy sky;
For he suddenly smote on the door, even
　Louder, and lifted his head:—
"Tell them I came, and no one answer'd,
　That I kept my word," he said.
Never the least stir made the listeners,
　Though every word he spake
Fell echoing through the shadowiness of the still house
　From the one man left awake:
Ay, they heard his foot upon the stirrup,
　And the sound of iron on stone,
And how the silence surged softly backward,
　When the plunging hoofs were gone.

WALTER DE LA MARE

THE SONG OF THE CYCLOPS

Brave iron, brave hammer, from your sound
The art of music has her ground;
On the anvil thou keep'st time,
Thy knick-a-knock is a smith's best chime.
    Yet thwick-a-thwack, thwick, thwack-a-thwack,
      thwack,
    Make our brawny sinews crack:
    Then pit-a-pat, pat, pit-a-pat, pat,
    Till thickest bars be beaten flat.

We shoe the horses of the sun,
Harness the dragons of the moon;
Forge Cupid's quiver, bow, and arrows,
And our dame's coach that's drawn with sparrows.
    Till thwick-a-thwack, etc.

Jove's roaring cannons and his rammers
We beat out with our Lemnian hammers;
Mars his gauntlet, helm, and spear,
And Gorgon shield are all made here.
    Till thwick-a-thwack, etc.

The grate which, shut, the day outbars,
Those golden studs, which nail the stars,
The globe's case and the axle-tree,
Who can hammer these but we?
    Till thwick-a-thwack, etc.

A warming-pan to heat earth's bed,
Lying i' the frozen zone half-dead;

Hob-nails to serve the man i' the moon,
And sparrowbills to clout Pan's shoon
  Whose work but ours?
  Till thwick-a-thwack, etc.

Venus' kettles, pots, and pans
We make, or else she brawls and bans;
Tongs, shovels, and irons have their places,
Else she scratches all our faces.
  Till thwick-a-thwack, thwick, thwack-a-thwack,
    thwack,
  Make our brawny sinews crack:
  Then pit-a-pat, pat, pit-a-pat, pat,
  Till thickest bars be beaten flat.

THOMAS DEKKER

THE FIDDLER OF DOONEY

When I play on my fiddle in Dooney,
Folk dance like a wave of the sea;
My cousin is priest in Kilvarnet,
My brother in Moharabuiee.

I passed my brother and cousin:
They read in their books of prayer;
I read in my book of songs
I bought at the Sligo fair.

When we come at the end of time
To Peter sitting in state,
He will smile on the three old spirits,
But call me first through the gate;

227

For the good are always the merry,
Save by an evil chance,
And the merry love the fiddle,
And the merry love to dance:

And when the folk there spy me,
They will all come up to me,
With " Here is the fiddler of Dooney! "
And dance like a wave of the sea.

WILLIAM BUTLER YEATS

Moharabuiee] pronounced " Mockrabwee ".

FROLIC

The children were shouting together
    And racing along the sands,
A glimmer of dancing shadows,
    A dovelike flutter of hands.

The stars were shouting in heaven,
    The sun was chasing the moon:
The game was the same as the children's.
    They danced to the self-same tune.

The whole of the world was merry,
    One joy from the vale to the height,
Where the blue woods of twilight encircled
    The lovely lawns of the light.

A.E.

THE SILVER PENNY

" Sailorman, I'll give to you
    My bright silver penny,
If out to sea you'll sail me
    And my dear sister Jenny."

" Get in, young sir, I'll sail ye
    And your dear sister Jenny,
But pay she shall her golden locks
    Instead of your penny."

They sail away, they sail away,
    O fierce the winds blew!
The foam flew in clouds
    And dark the night grew!

And all the green sea-water
    Climbed steep into the boat;
Back to the shore again
    Sail they will not.

Drowned is the sailorman,
    Drowned is sweet Jenny,
And drowned in the deep sea
    A bright silver penny.

                    WALTER DE LA MARE

SEA FEVER

I must down to the seas again, to the lonely sea and the
    sky,
And all I ask is a tall ship and a star to steer her by,

And the wheel's kick and the wind's song and the white
  sail's shaking,
And a grey mist on the sea's face and a grey dawn
  breaking.

I must down to the seas again, for the call of the running
  tide
Is a wild call and a clear call that may not be denied;
And all I ask is a windy day with the white clouds flying,
And the flung spray and the blown spume, and the sea-
  gulls crying.

I must down to the seas again, to the vagrant gypsy life,
To the gull's way and the whale's way where the wind's
  like a whetted knife;
And all I ask is a merry yarn from a laughing fellow-
  rover,
And quiet sleep and a sweet dream when the long trick's
  over.

JOHN MASEFIELD

SMELLS

Why is it that the poets tell
So little of the sense of smell?
These are the odours I love well:

The smell of coffee freshly ground;
Or rich plum pudding, holly-crowned;
Or onions fried and deeply browned.

The fragrance of a fumy pipe;
The smell of apples, newly ripe;
And printers' ink on leaden type.

Woods by moonlight in September
Breathe most sweet; and I remember
Many a smoky camp-fire ember.

Camphor, turpentine, and tea,
The balsam of a Christmas tree,
These are whiffs of gramarye . . .
A ship smells best of all to me!

CHRISTOPHER MORLEY

gramarye] magic.

SILVER

Slowly, silently, now the moon
Walks the night in her silver shoon;
This way, and that, she peers, and sees
Silver fruit upon silver trees;
One by one the casements catch
Her beams beneath the silvery thatch;
Couched in his kennel, like a log,
With paws of silver sleeps the dog;
From their shadowy cote the white breasts peep
Of doves in a silver-feathered sleep;
A harvest mouse goes scampering by,
With silver claws, and silver eye;
And moveless fish in the water gleam,
By silver reeds in a silver stream.

WALTER DE LA MARE

231

THE LANDSCAPE NEAR AN AERODROME

More beautiful and soft than any moth
With burring furred antennae feeling its huge path
Through dusk, the air-liner with shut-off engines
Glides over suburbs and the sleeves set trailing tall
To point the wind. Gently, broadly, she falls
Scarcely disturbing charted currents of air.
Lulled by descent, the travellers across sea
And across feminine land indulging its easy limbs
In miles of softness, now let their eyes trained by
    watching
Penetrate through dusk the outskirts of this town
Here where industry shows a fraying edge.
Here they may see what is being done.

Beyond the winking masthead light
And the landing-ground, they observe the outposts
Of work: chimneys like lank black fingers
Or figures frightening and mad: the squat buildings
With their strange air behind trees, like women's faces
Shattered by grief. Here where few houses
Moan with faint light behind their blinds
They remark the unhomely sense of complaint, like a
    dog
Shut out and shivering at the foreign moon.

In the last sweep of love, they pass over fields
Behind the aerodrome, where boys play all day
Hacking dead grass: whose cries, like wild birds,
Settle upon the nearest roofs
But soon are hid under the loud city.

Then, as they land, they hear the tolling bell
Reaching across the landscape of hysteria
To where, larger than all the charcoaled batteries
And imaged towers against that dying sky,
Religion stands, the church blocking the sun.

STEPHEN SPENDER

WORDS

Out of us all
That make rhymes,
Will you choose
Sometimes—
As the winds use
A crack in a wall
Or a drain,
Their joy or their pain
To whistle through—
Choose me,
You English words?

I know you:
You are light as dreams,
Tough as oak,
Precious as gold,
As poppies and corn,
Or an old cloak;
Sweet as our birds
To the ear,
As the burnet rose

In the heat
Of Midsummer:

H*

Strange as the races
Of dead and unborn:.
Strange and sweet
Equally,
And familiar,
To the eye,
As the dearest faces
That a man knows,
And as lost homes are:
But though older far
Than oldest yew,—
As our hills are, old,—
Worn new
Again and again:
Young as our streams
After rain:
And as dear
As the earth which you prove
That we love.

Make me content
With some sweetness
From Wales,
Whose nightingales
Have no wings,—
From Wiltshire and Kent
And Herefordshire,
And the villages there,—
From the names, and the things
No less.
Let me sometimes dance
With you,

Or climb,
Or stand perchance
In ecstasy,
Fixed and free
In a rhyme,
As poets do.

EDWARD THOMAS

FLEET STREET

I never see the newsboys run
   Amid the whirling street,
   With swift untiring feet,
To cry the latest venture done,
But I expect one day to hear
   Them cry the crack of doom
   And risings from the tomb,
With great Archangel Michael near;
And see them running from the Fleet
   As messengers of God,
   With Heaven's tidings shod
About their brave unwearied feet.

SHANE LESLIE

PIBROCH OF DONUIL DHU

Pibroch of Donuil Dhu,
   Pibroch of Donuil,
Wake thy wild voice anew,
   Summon Clan Conuil.

pibroch] martial notes from the bagpipes.

235

Come away, come away,
    Hark to the summons!
Come in your war array,
    Gentles and commons!

Come from deep glen, and
    From mountain so rocky,
The war-pipe and pennon
    Are at Inverlochy.
Come every hill-plaid, and
    True heart that wears one,
Come every steel blade, and
    Strong hand that bears one.

Leave untended the herd,
    The flock without shelter;
Leave the corpse uninterred,
    The bride at the altar.
Leave the deer, leave the steer,
    Leave nets and barges;
Come with your fighting-gear,
    Broadswords and targes.

Come as the winds come, when
    Forests are rended:
Come as the waves come, when
    Navies are stranded:
Faster come, faster come,
    Faster and faster,
Chief, vassal, page, and groom,
    Tenant and master.

Fast they come, fast they come;
    See how they gather!

Wide waves the eagle plume,
   Blended with heather.
Cast your plaids, draw your blades,
   Forward, each man, set!
Pibroch of Donuil Dhu,
   Knell for the onset!

SIR WALTER SCOTT

THE PATRIOT

It was roses, roses, all the way,
   With myrtle mixed in my path like mad:
The house-roofs seemed to heave and sway,
   The church-spires flamed, such flags they had,
A year ago on this very day!

The air broke into a mist with bells,
   The old walls rocked with the crowd and cries.
Had I said, " Good folk, mere noise repels—
   But give me your sun from yonder skies! "
They had answered, " And afterward, what else? "

Alack, it was I who leaped at the sun
   To give it my loving friends to keep!
Nought man could do, have I left undone:
   And you see my harvest, what I reap
This very day, now a year is run.

There's nobody on the house-tops now—
   Just a palsied few at the windows set;
For the best of the sight is, all allow,
   At the Shambles' Gate—or, better yet,
By the very scaffold's foot, I trow.

I go in the rain, and, more than needs,
  A rope cuts both my wrists behind;
And I think, by the feel, my forehead bleeds,
  For they fling, whoever has a mind,
Stones at me for my year's misdeeds.

Thus I entered, and thus I go!
  In triumphs, people have dropped down dead.
"Paid by the world,—what dost thou owe
  Me?"—God might question; now instead,
'Tis God shall repay: I am safer so.

ROBERT BROWNING

THE DYING PATRIOT

Day breaks on England down the Kentish hills,
Singing in the silence of the meadow-footing rills,
    Day of my day, O day!
  I saw them march from Dover, long ago,
  With a silver cross before them, singing low,
Monks of Rome from their home where the blue seas
        break in foam,
    Augustine with his feet of snow.

Noon strikes on England, noon on Oxford town,
—Beauty she was statue cold—there's blood upon her
        gown:
Noon of my dreams, O noon!
  Proud and godly kings had built her, long ago,
  With her towers and tombs and statues all arow,
With her fair and floral air and the love that lingers
        there
    And the streets where the great men go.

Evening on the olden, the golden sea of Wales,
When the first star shivers and the last wave pales:
O evening dreams!
　There's a house that Britons walked in, long ago,
　Where now the springs of ocean fall and flow,
And the dead robed in red and sea-lilies overhead
　Sway when the long winds blow.

Sleep not, my country: though night is here, afar
Your children of the morning are clamorous for war:
Fire in the night, O dreams!
　Though she send you as she sent you, long ago,
　South to desert, east to ocean, west to snow,
West of these out to seas colder than the Hebrides I must
　　go
　Where the fleet of stars is anchored and the young
　　star-captains go.

JAMES ELROY FLECKER

ANTHEM FOR DOOMED YOUTH

What passing-bells for these who die as cattle?
Only the monstrous anger of the guns.
Only the stuttering rifles' rapid rattle
Can patter out their hasty orisons.
No mockeries for them; no prayers nor bells,
Nor any voice of mourning save the choirs,—
The shrill, demented choirs of wailing shells;
And bugles calling for them from sad shires.

What candles may be held to speed them all?
Not in the hands of boys, but in their eyes
Shall shine the holy glimmers of good-byes.

The pallor of girls' brows shall be their pall;
Their flowers the tenderness of patient minds,
And each slow dusk a drawing-down of blinds.

WILFRED OWEN

CORONACH

(From " The Lady of the Lake ")

He is gone on the mountain,
  He is lost to the forest,
Like a summer-dried fountain,
  When our need was the sorest,
The font, reappearing,
  From the rain-drops shall borrow,
But to us comes no cheering,
  To Duncan no morrow!

The hand of the reaper
  Takes the ears that are hoary,
But the voice of the weeper
  Wails manhood in glory.
The autumn winds rushing
  Waft the leaves that are searest,
But our flower was in flushing,
  When blighting was nearest.

Fleet foot on the correi,
  Sage counsel in cumber,
Red hand in the foray,
  How sound is thy slumber!

Like the dew on the mountain,
  Like the foam on the river,
Like the bubble on the fountain,
  Thou art gone, and for ever!

SIR WALTER SCOTT

Coronach] a funeral song in the Highlands.
correi] mountain hollow where stags gather.
cumber] trouble or distress.

THE LOST LEADER

Just for a handful of silver he left us,
  Just for a riband to stick in his coat—
Found the one gift of which fortune bereft us,
  Lost all the others she lets us devote;
They, with the gold to give, doled him out silver,
  So much was theirs who so little allowed:
How all our copper had gone for his service!
  Rags—were they purple, his heart had been proud!
We that had loved him so, followed him, honoured him
  Lived in his mild and magnificent eye,
Learned his great language, caught his clear accents,
  Made him our pattern to live and to die!
Shakespeare was of us, Milton was for us,
  Burns, Shelley, were with us,—they watch from their
    graves!
He alone breaks from the van and the freemen,
  He alone sinks to the rear and the slaves!

We shall march prospering,—not thro' his presence;
  Songs may inspirit us,—not from his lyre;

Deeds will be done,—while he boasts his quiescence,
  Still bidding crouch whom the rest bade aspire:
Blot out his name, then, record one lost soul more,
  One task more declined, one more footpath untrod,
One more triumph for devils and sorrow for angels,
  One wrong more to man, one more insult to God!
Life's night begins: let him never come back to us!
  There would be doubt, hesitation, and pain,
Forced praise on our part—the glimmer of twilight,
  Never glad confident morning again!
Best fight on well, for we taught him,—strike gallantly,
  Menace our heart ere we master his own;
Then let him receive the new knowledge and wait us,
  Pardoned in Heaven, the first by the throne!

                                    ROBERT BROWNING

LA BELLE DAME SANS MERCI

O, what can ail thee, knight-at-arms,
Alone and palely loitering?
The sedge is withered from the lake,
And no birds sing!

O, what can ail thee, knight-at-arms,
So haggard and so woe-begone?
The squirrel's granary is full,
And the harvest's done.

I see a lily on thy brow,
With anguish moist and fever dew;
And on thy cheek a fading rose
Fast withereth too—

I met a lady in the meads
Full beautiful, a faery's child;
Her hair was long, her foot was light,
And her eyes were wild—

I made a garland for her head,
And bracelets too, and fragrant zone;
She look'd at me as she did love
And made sweet moan—

I set her on my pacing steed,
And nothing else saw all day long;
For sideways would she lean, and sing
A faery's song—

She found me roots of relish sweet,
And honey wild, and manna dew;
And sure in language strange she said,
I love thee true—

She took me to her elfin grot,
And there she gaz'd and sighed full sore,
And there I shut her wild, wild eyes
With kisses four.

And there she lullèd me asleep,
And there I dream'd, ah woe betide,
The latest dream I ever dreamed
On the cold hill side.

I saw pale kings, and princes too,
Pale warriors, death-pale were they all;
Who cried—" La belle Dame sans Merci
Hath thee in thrall! "

I saw their starv'd lips in the gloam
With horrid warning gapèd wide,
And I awoke and found me here
On the cold hill side.

And this is why I sojourn here
Alone and palely loitering,
Though the sedge is withered from the lake,
And no birds sing.

JOHN KEATS

This is the original version as given from Colvin: *Keats, His Life and Poetry*, 1917. The version printed in Leigh Hunt's *Indicator*, 1820, contains several changes in the text.

BIOGRAPHICAL NOTES ON AUTHORS

ABERCROMBIE, LASCELLES. 1881-1938. Formerly Professor of English Literature, Bedford College. A well-known poet and critic, whose *Collected Poems* are included in the Oxford Poets.

A.E. (George William Russell). 1867-1935. An Irish poet and dramatist, whose poetry was described by his contemporary, William Butler Yeats, as "The most delicate and subtle that any Irishman of our time has written".

ARNOLD, MATTHEW. 1822-1888. The son of the famous Headmaster of Rugby School, whose zeal as a reformer he inherited. Although he had previously published *The Strayed Reveller* and *Empedocles on Etna*, it was with the *Poems* of 1853 that he won fame. This volume, which contained *Sohrab and Rustum* and *The Scholar Gipsy*, included his famous preface in which he shows that his approach to poetry is that of one who sets before himself the best models and will be content with nothing short of perfection.

BELLOC, HILAIRE. Born 1870. A well-known writer of essays, biographies, historical works, verse and travel books. He was born in France and as a youth served as a conscript in the French army. Some of his most delightful works include: *The Path to Rome*, *Cautionary Tales* and *Hills and the Sea*.

BLUNDEN, EDMUND CHARLES. Born 1896. A poet who delights in rural sights and sounds. As a young man he served as a subaltern in the first world war and afterwards he wrote *Undertones of War*, which is not only one of the best war books, but is full of the essence of poetry.

BROOKE, RUPERT. 1887-1915. One of the most famous of the war poets. He joined the Royal Naval Division in 1914, and died in the Dardanelles in the following April.

BROWNING, ROBERT. 1812-1889. Browning was the son of a clerk in the Bank of England. His first poem, *Pauline*, appeared in 1833. In 1846 he married the poetess, Elizabeth Barrett, and lived with her in Italy until her death in 1861, when he returned to London with his son. His vivid narrative poems and dramatic monologues remain popular.

BURNS, ROBERT. 1759-1796. A ploughboy who became the greatest and most beloved of Scottish poets. After farming in partnership with his brother for four years, during which he wrote such poems as *The Cotter's Saturday Night, To a Mouse* and *To a Mountain Daisy*, he decided to emigrate to Jamaica. For this purpose he raised money by publishing the Kilmarnock edition of these early poems. The fame which the publication brought him caused him to be lionized in the Edinburgh society of the day. Besides enriching our literature with many beautiful lyrics, Burns adapted or re-wrote numbers of old songs which might otherwise have been forgotten.

BYRON, LORD GEORGE GORDON. 1788-1824. The son of Mad Jack, a profligate sea captain and the grandson of Admiral John Byron, a gallant naval officer and an explorer whose misfortunes earned him the nickname of Foul Weather John. The young Byron, who was a cripple, came into the family title at the tender age of ten. In spite of his club foot he played cricket for Harrow, and after leaving that school he continued his education at Cambridge. *Childe Harold's Pilgrimage* was written shortly after he returned from his travels on the Continent and in the Near East, and this and the poems which followed swiftly from his fluent pen brought him immense fame. His greatest work, however, is probably *Don Juan*, which he wrote just before he took up the cause of freedom in Greece. He died at Missolonghi in April 1824.

CARMAN, BLISS. 1861-1929. Born at Fredericktown, New Brunswick. After some journalistic work in U.S.A. he devoted himself more and more to literary work. He has been teacher, editor, and civil engineer.

CARROLL, LEWIS (Charles Lutwidge Dodgson). 1832-1898. A lecturer in Mathematics at Oxford, whose friendship for Alice Pleasaunce Liddell, an enchanting, lovely child of seven, led him first to tell her the famous story of *Alice in Wonderland* and later to send it to a publisher. His stories appeal not only to children, but by their humour and logical absurdity to many grown-up people.

CHESTERTON, GILBERT KEITH. 1874-1936. The son of a Kensington estate agent. He wrote many essays, poems and short stories as well as works of criticism and biography.

CLARE, JOHN. 1793-1864. The son of an agricultural labourer, he was herd boy, vagrant and farmer by turns, and became insane in 1837.

COLERIDGE, SAMUEL TAYLOR. 1772-1834. The son of the vicar of Ottery St. Mary and a fellow pupil at Christ's Hospital with Charles

Lamb. After a very brief experience of military service in the 15th Dragoons, he returned to Cambridge. In 1795 he met Wordsworth, with whom he published the famous *Lyrical Ballads*—a collection of poems which included not only his own *Ancient Mariner*, but also Wordsworth's *Lines composed above Tintern Abbey*. The mysterious beauty of his poetry and its haunting rhythms are perhaps Coleridge's chief contributions.

COLUM, PADRAIC. Born in Ireland in 1881, but now resident in New York. He wrote several plays for the Abbey Theatre.

COWPER, WILLIAM. 1731-1800. A sensitive, shy and retiring poet, whose timidity as a boy made him the victim of bullying at school. After reading law he actually attempted suicide to avoid the ordeal of presenting himself for a public examination. Retiring into the country, where he wrote the famous Olney Hymns, he there became acquainted with Lady Austen, who set him the task of writing a long poem about the sofa in his room. The result was *The Task*, in which the poet describes with delightful felicity the sights and sounds of the English countryside. His sensibility was attractive to people of fashion of his day and his humour at times seems to anticipate that of the Victorian novelist, Charles Dickens.

CUNNINGHAM, ALLAN. 1784-1842. A stonemason and a native of Dumfriesshire. Among his best-known poems are: *A Wet Sheet and a Flowing Sea* and *Hame, Hame, Hame*.

DAVIES, WILLIAM HENRY. 1871-1940. He has told the story of his life as a tramp and a pedlar in *The Autobiography of a Super-Tramp*, which also describes how he first began to jot down his early poems that later brought him fame.

DAVIDSON, JOHN. 1857-1909. A Scottish schoolmaster who came to London in 1889. Although he wrote plays and novels, his most important work was as a poet.

DEKKER, THOMAS. 1570-1632. A Londoner who suffered from poverty in his youth and later wrote many plays, some in collaboration with Michael Drayton, Ben Jonson and others. Amongst his plays is *The Shoemaker's Holiday*.

DE LA MARE, WALTER. Born 1873. One of the chief poets of our own time whose path to fame has been slow but sure. His verse is at once original and natural, and his exquisite artistry touches everything he writes with magic and enchantment. His first volume of verse was published under the pseudonym of Walter Ramal in 1903.

DRAYTON, MICHAEL. 1563-1631. Born at Hartshill in Warwickshire and may have had some employment at court. His ambitious *Poly-Olbion* and *The Barons' Wars*, and other historical as well as sacred poems are little read, but few people are unacquainted with *Nimphidia*, one of our most famous fairy poems, and one or two of his sonnets and ballads, e.g. *Since There's No Help, Come Let Us Kiss and Part* and *Fair Stood the Wind for France*.

DRINKWATER, JOHN. 1882-1937. A poet and dramatist who is famous for a number of historical plays, including *Abraham Lincoln* and *Oliver Cromwell*.

FLECKER, JAMES ELROY. 1884-1915. He entered the consular service and spent two years in Beirut. *Hassan*, a verse drama which appeared in 1922, was a popular success. Above all else he had a great facility in his use of expressive words.

GIBSON, WILFRID WILSON. Born 1878. Gibson served in the ranks in the first world war and his *Collected Poems* reveal the wealth of poetry he has contributed to our literature. He is one of the best of contemporary narrative poets.

GLEN, WILLIAM. 1789-1826. William Glen was born in Glasgow and became a merchant in the West Indian trade, residing for a time in one of the West Indian islands. After meeting misfortune in his business affairs, he finally settled down in the parish of Aberfoyle, where he spent the last years of his life.

GOLDSMITH, OLIVER. 1730-1774. The son of an Irish clergyman, he came to London in 1756 and commenced his literary career as a hack writer. His friend, Samuel Johnson, whom he met in 1761, had a high opinion of his talents and there are many interesting references to him in Boswell. Goldsmith's *Vicar of Wakefield*, *She Stoops to Conquer* and *The Deserted Village* not only won him fame in his day as a novelist, a dramatist and a poet, but they still retain their popularity.

GRAY, THOMAS. 1716-1771. The son of a scrivener of violent temper. He owed it to his mother and his aunt that he received a liberal education at Eton, not far from the churchyard of Stoke Poges, which he was to immortalize in his most famous work.

HARDY, THOMAS. 1840-1928. The son of a builder, he made a great reputation as a novelist. Later he abandoned novel writing for poetry, his first love, and became one of the greatest poets of his time.

HERRICK, ROBERT. 1591-1674. The son of a prosperous goldsmith, he was born in London in 1591. He was the friend and admirer of Ben Jonson. His best work is to be found in *Hesperides*.

HODGSON, RALPH. Born 1871. A poet whose output is very small, but one who has rare gifts, as shown by the two long poems *The Bull* and *The Song of Honour*.

HOGG, JAMES. 1770-1835. The " Ettrick Shepherd ", who was discovered by Sir Walter Scott. He was born in Ettrick Forest and began life as a shepherd. In later life he combined farming with literary work.

HOLMES, OLIVER WENDELL. 1809-1894. An American professor of anatomy and physiology, whose humorous essays published under titles such as *The Professor at the Breakfast Table*, were widely read in the second half of the nineteenth century. Some of his lyrics and humorous poems are still widely appreciated.

HOOD, THOMAS. 1799-1845. The son of a bookseller and the editor of a number of periodicals. He is chiefly remembered for his humorous work.

KEATS, JOHN. 1795-1821. The son of a livery-stable keeper in London. He qualified as a surgeon, but gave up surgery for poetry. In his short life of twenty-five years he produced master-pieces which justify comparison with the work of the greatest of English poets.

KINGSLEY, CHARLES. 1819-1875. Born at Holne in Devonshire. He became Rector of Eversley in Hampshire and, later, Professor of Modern History at Cambridge. He was deeply interested in social questions and his own type of religion became known as " muscular Christianity ". Among his various writings are the popular *Westward Ho*, *Hereward the Wake*, *The Heroes*, *The Water Babies* and many spirited songs and ballads.

LESLIE, SIR SHANE. Born 1885. The eldest son of Sir John Leslie. Educated at Eton and King's College, Cambridge. Author of a number of biographies and several volumes of verse.

LOWELL, JAMES RUSSELL. 1819-1891. An American poet who succeeded Longfellow as Professor of Belles Lettres at Harvard. He edited at one time the *Atlantic Monthly*. His volumes of verse include the *Biglow Paper*.

MARRYAT, FREDERICK. 1792-1848. A captain in the Royal Navy who served with distinction in the first Burmese war. He wrote many exciting and amusing stories of life at sea, based on his own experiences, e.g. *Mr. Midshipman Easy*, and *Peter Simple*.

MASEFIELD, JOHN. Born 1878. As a boy Masefield ran away to sea and on returning to England he joined the staff of *The Manchester Guardian*. In 1930 he succeeded Robert Bridges as Poet Laureate. While many think that his best work is to be found in his longer poems, such as *Reynard the Fox*, he has written many unforgettable lyrics of great beauty. Vivid reminiscences of his early seafaring career lend colour and verisimilitude to many of his writings in prose and verse, particularly to *Dauber*.

MONRO, HAROLD. 1879-1932. Educated at Radley and Cambridge.

In 1911 he founded the *Poetry Review* and the Poetry Bookshop in the following year.

MORLEY, CHRISTOPHER. Born 1890. An American who came to Oxford University as a Rhodes Scholar, and a publisher and writer of novels and essays.

NAIRNE, BARONESS CAROLINA. 1766-1845. She wrote a number of Jacobite songs and ballads as well as the well-known *Land o' the Leal.* After her death her poems were collected and published under the title of *Lays from Strathearn.*

NOEL T 1799-1861. Famous for his song, *Rocked in the Cradle of the Deep.*

NOYES, ALFRED. Born 1880. His tales in verse, which include *Tales of the Mermaid Tavern,* have won considerable popularity.

O'NEILL, MOIRA. The pseudonym of Mrs. Skrine. Her *Songs of the Glens of Antrim* were published in 1902.

O'SULLIVAN, SEUMAS. Born 1879. The author of *The Twilight People, Collected Poems* and other writings. He is the editor of *The Dublin Magazine.*

OWEN, WILFRED. 1893-1918. A young poet, full of promise, who met his death as an infantry officer in the First World War. His *Strange Meeting* was regarded by some as the most memorable poem of its time.

POE, EDGAR ALLAN. 1809-1849. The son of actor parents, born in Boston, Mass., in 1809. On coming to England as a boy, he was sent to a school in Stoke Newington. When he returned to America he had already begun to find his bent as a writer before he joined the American army, from which he obtained his discharge a few years later. His remarkable tales of mystery and imagination were one of the landmarks in the history of the short story, and in addition he wrote some notable verse.

POPE, ALEXANDER. 1688-1744. The son of a London linen-draper, he spent most of his life at his river-side home at Twickenham, not far from the scene laid in *The Rape of the Lock.* Of Pope, Professor Saintsbury said that he was within certain narrow limits one of the greatest masters of poetic form that the world has ever seen, and a considerable, though sometimes overrated satirist. From the writings of no other poet with the exception of Shakespeare have so many phrases passed into common use, for his eloquence cloaked his somewhat commonplace philosophy in an extraordinarily attractive garb.

QUILLER-COUCH, SIR ARTHUR. 1863-1944. A Cornishman who customarily wrote under the pseudonym of " Q " and became Professor of English Literature at Cambridge. Besides completing

St. Ives, which R. L. Stevenson had left unfinished at his death, " Q " wrote a number of stories including *The Splendid Spur* and the charming tales about Troy Town (Fowey). He edited the *Oxford Book of English Verse* and the equally famous *Oxford Book of Ballads.* Among his most characteristic prose writings are his delightful essays *On the Art of Writing* and *On the Art of Reading.*

SCOTT, SIR WALTER. 1771-1832. He was called to the Bar in 1792 after an apprenticeship to his father, a writer to the signet in Edinburgh. His longer romantic poems were very popular, but were outstripped by the enormous success of the long series of Waverley novels that followed. The story of Scott's heroic struggle to pay his creditors is told in his life by Lockhart.

SHAKESPEARE, WILLIAM. 1564-1616. In spite of countless books on Shakespeare, we know very little of his life. He was the son of a glover of Stratford-on-Avon, and was educated at the local Grammar School, which is still in existence. About 1586 he arrived in London and became known as an actor and writer of plays. When the theatres reopened in May 1594, he joined the Lord Chamberlain's company for good, afterwards becoming part-proprietor of the Globe. When he retired about 1600 he was able to return to Stratford-on-Avon and purchase the best house in his native town.

SHELLEY, PERCY BYSSHE. 1792-1822. Shelley was born at Horsham, Sussex, and was educated at Eton and University College, Oxford. In appearance he was the most poetical of all the English poets, with the exception, perhaps, of Rupert Brooke. His voice, how-ever, was singularly unmelodious. He was drowned in a sudden storm in the Gulf of Spezzia.

SPENDER, STEPHEN. Born 1909. After leaving Oxford, Spender travelled widely. In the second world war he served as an air-raid warden and he has written a book describing his experiences.

STEPHENS, JAMES. Born 1882. An Irishman who has written some charming poetry as well as novels, fairy-tales and short stories.

STEVENSON, ROBERT LOUIS. 1850-1894. He was born in Edinburgh and studied engineering and then the law. Lung trouble drove him abroad in search of health and some of his travels are described in his books. He was a deliberate and conscious artist in words and admitted to playing the sedulous ape to other masters of style—an apprenticeship which served him well when he came to write the books by which he is remembered.

TENNYSON, ALFRED, LORD. 1809-1892. Tennyson was born at Somersby where his father was rector. He succeeded Wordsworth as Poet Laureate in 1850, and wrote some superb lyrics, but his contemporaries usually admired his work for what was least admirable in it.

THOMAS EDWARD. 1878-1917. The author of several books on the English countryside, he turned later to poetry. His *Poems* (1917) and *Last Poems* (1918) appeared about the time he was killed in action in the First World War.

THORNBURY, GEORGE WALTER. 1828-1876. A journalist who was associated with Charles Dickens in *Household Words* and *All the Year Round*. He wrote both novels and poems.

WOLFE CHARLES. 1791-1823. Educated at Trinity College, Dublin, and later curate of Donoughmore, County Down. His famous poem *The Burial of Sir John Moore* was evidently based on Southey's narrative contributed to the *Annual Register*. It first appeared anonymously in the *Newry Telegraph*.

WORDSWORTH, WILLIAM. 1770-1850. He was the son of an attorney of Cockermouth. In the years immediately preceding the French Revolution, he paid two visits to France, where his youthful enthusiasm was kindled by the ideals of the revolutionaries. Later, when the Terror with its guillotine followed, his enthusiasm turned to deep pessimism. He then changed his politics and became an ardent patriot. Wordsworth is one of the greatest of our poets. He succeeded Southey as Poet Laureate in 1843.

YEATS, WILLIAM BUTLER. 1865-1939. Born in Dublin, he was fascinated in early boyhood by hearing the stories and legends from the country folk of Sligo. This prompted him to steep himself in Irish history and later he read widely, making a special study of the French poets. Ever seeking beauty, he abandoned his early style for the ornate verse of his later years. Yeats, who is one of the greatest of our modern poets, was the leading figure in the Irish literary revival.

YOUNG, ANDREW. Born 1885. A Scottish minister who later became a Church of England parson. His *Collected Poems* were published in 1936.

INDEX TO FIRST LINES